country classics

Music arranged and processed by Barnes Music Engraving Ltd
East Sussex TN22 4HA, UK

Design and Typesetting by Xheight Limited

Published 1995

ANNIE'S SONG
Words and Music by
JOHN DENVER
Moderately
D
Dsus4
D
mf
1. You fill up my
G
A
Bm
G
(1.3.) sen - ses like a night in a
(2.) love you, let me give my life
sim.
D
D/C♯
Bm7
D/A
fo - rest, like the moun - tains in
to you, let me drown in your
G
F♯m
Em
G
A7
spring - time, like a walk in the rain.
laugh - ter, let me die in your arms.

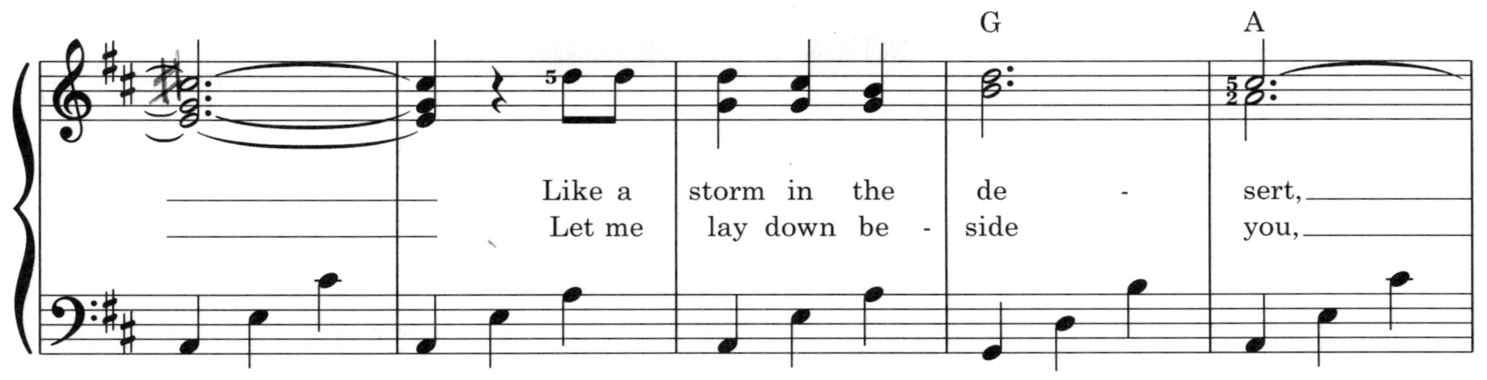
G
A
Like a storm in the de - sert,
Let me lay down be - side you,

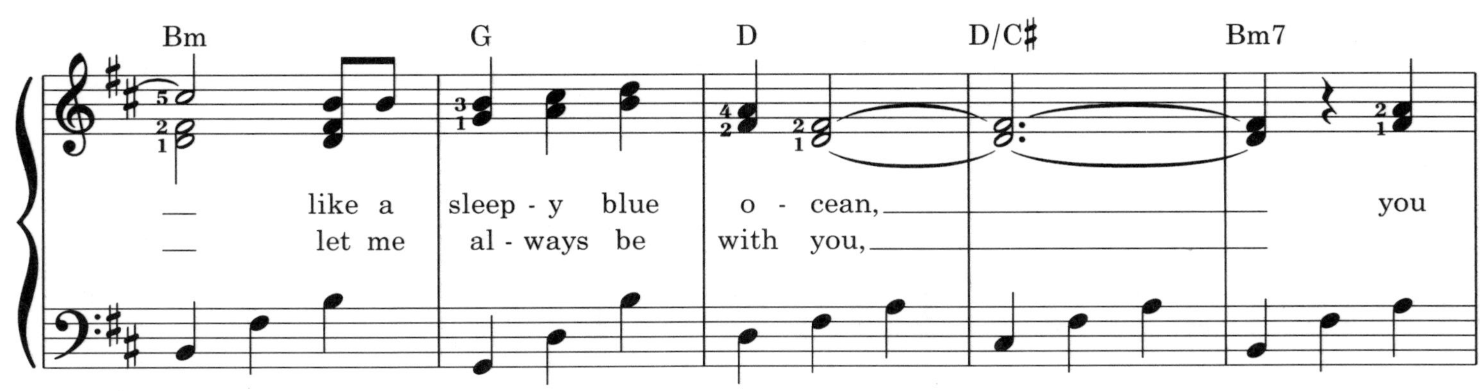
Bm
G
D
D/C♯
Bm7
like a sleep - y blue o - cean, you
let me al - ways be with you,

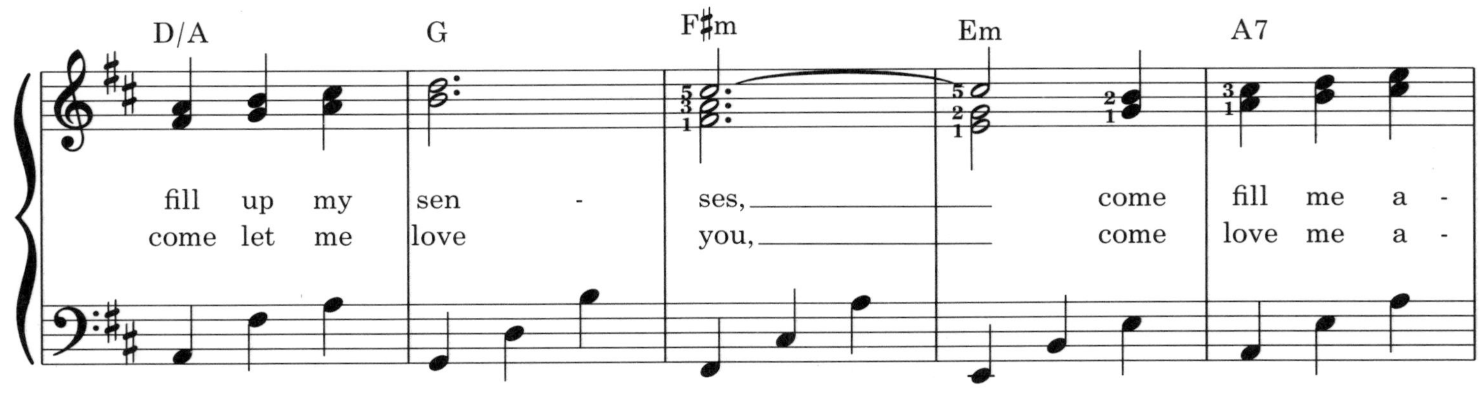
D/A
G
F♯m
Em
A7
fill up my sen - ses, come fill me a -
come let me love you, come love me a -

1.2.
3.
D
Dsus4
D
D
- gain. 2. Come let me
- gain. 3. You fill up my

BY THE TIME I GET TO PHOENIX

Words and Music by
JIM WEBB

Verse 2
By the time I make Albuquerque she'll be workin'
She'll prob'ly stop at lunch and give me a call
But she'll just hear that phone
Keep on ringin' off the wall
That's all

Verse 3
By the time I make Oklahoma she'll be sleepin'
She'll turn softly and call my name out low
And she'll cry just to think that I'd really leave her
Tho' time and time I've tried to tell her so
She just didn't know I would really go

CONSTANT CRAVING

Words and Music by
K D LANG and BEN MINK

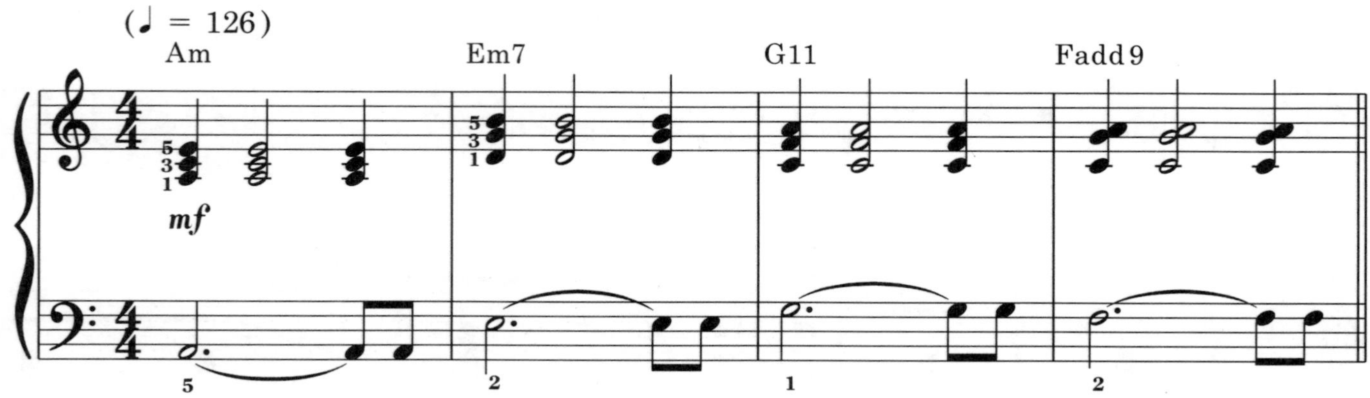

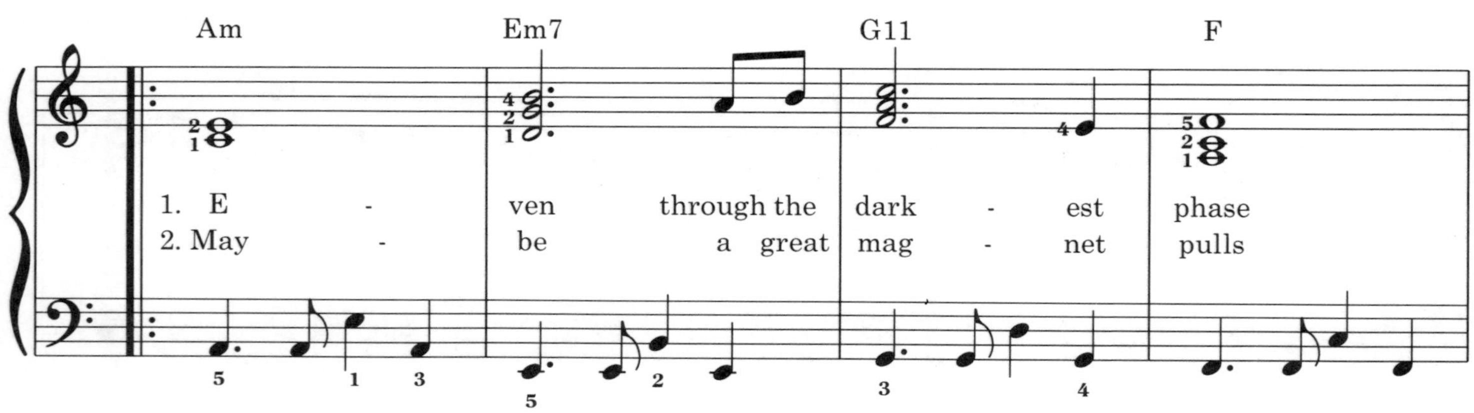

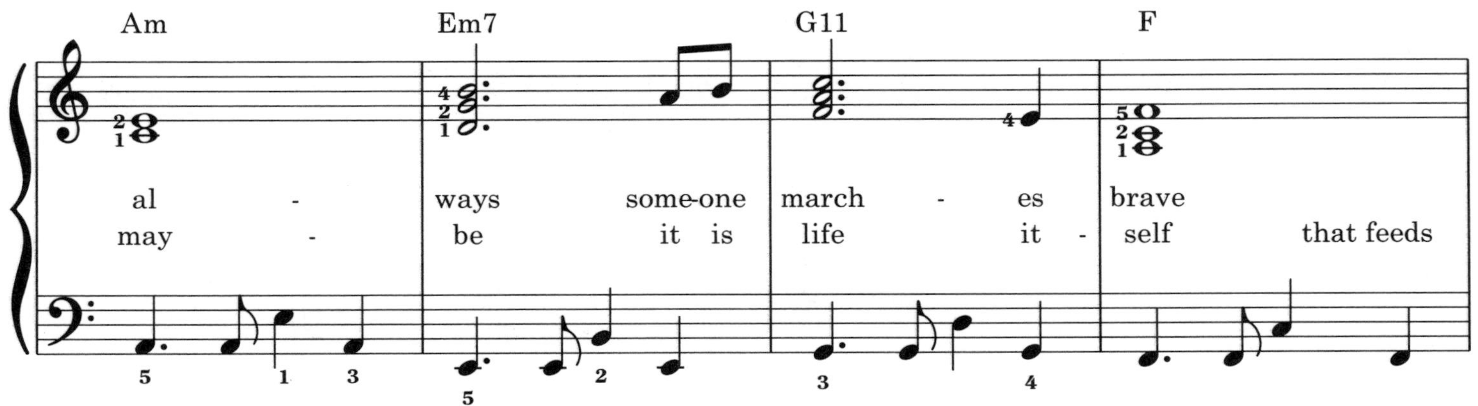
Am
Em7
G11
F
al - ways some-one march - es brave
may - be it is life it - self that feeds

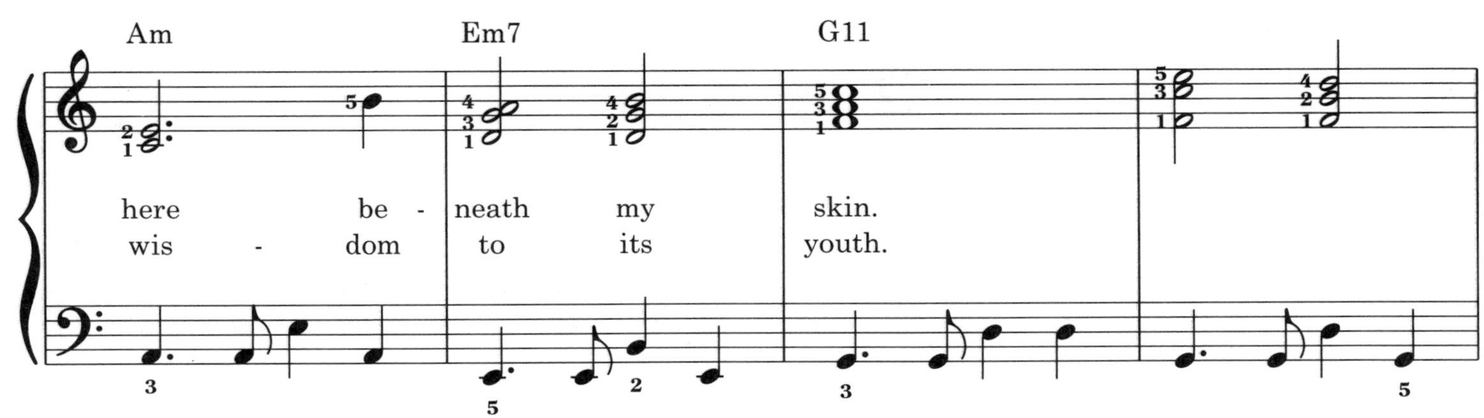
Am
Em7
G11
here be - neath my skin.
wis - dom to its youth.

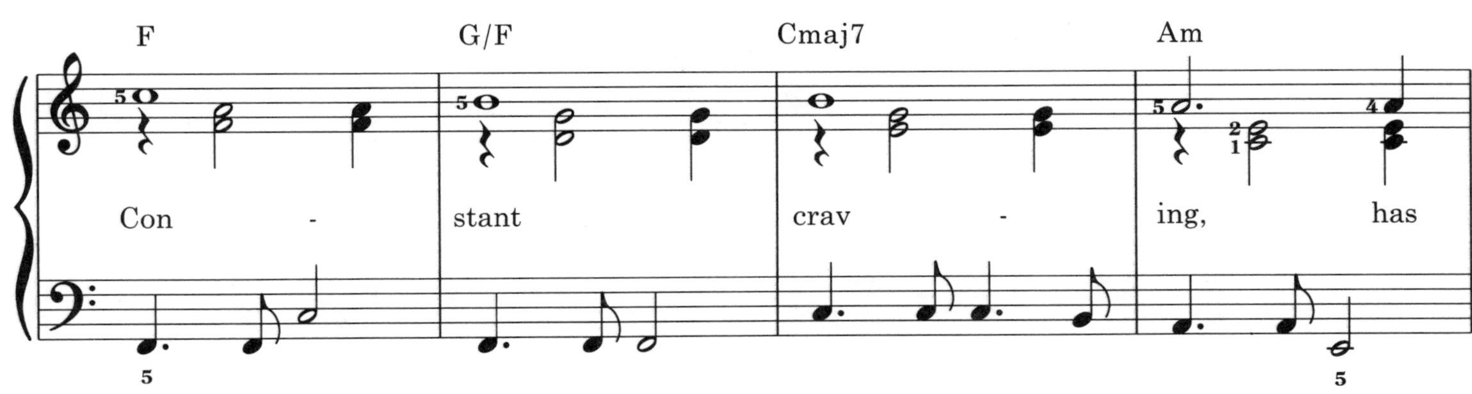
F
G/F
Cmaj7
Am
Con - stant crav - ing, has

B♭maj7
B♭
1.
Am
al - ways been.

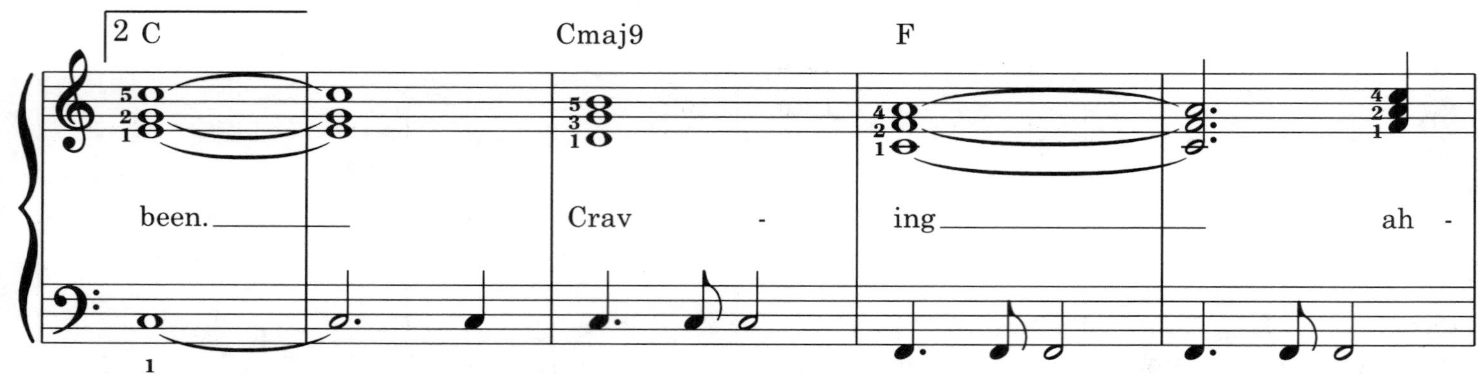
2 C
Cmaj9
F
been.
Crav - ing
ah -

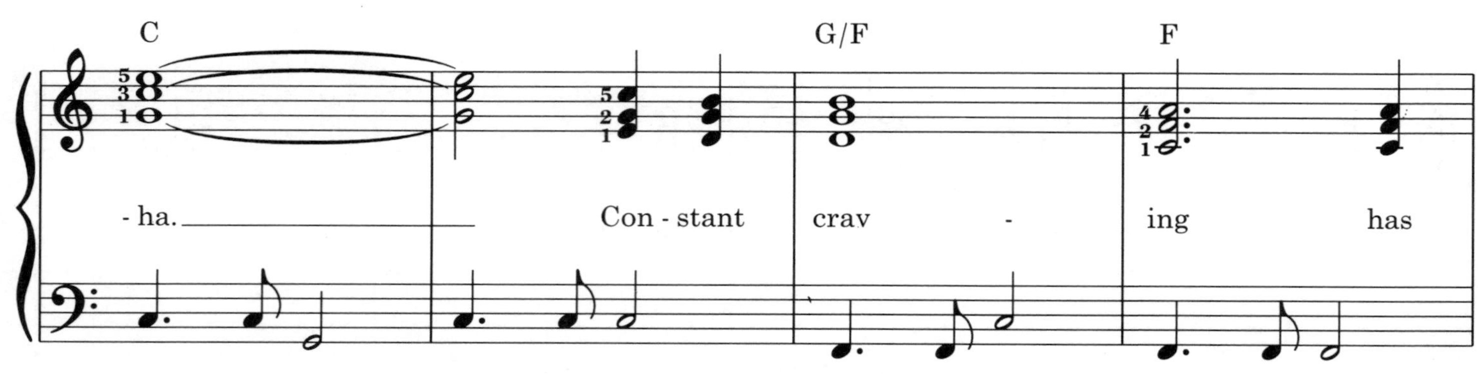
C
G/F
F
- ha.
Con - stant
crav - ing
has

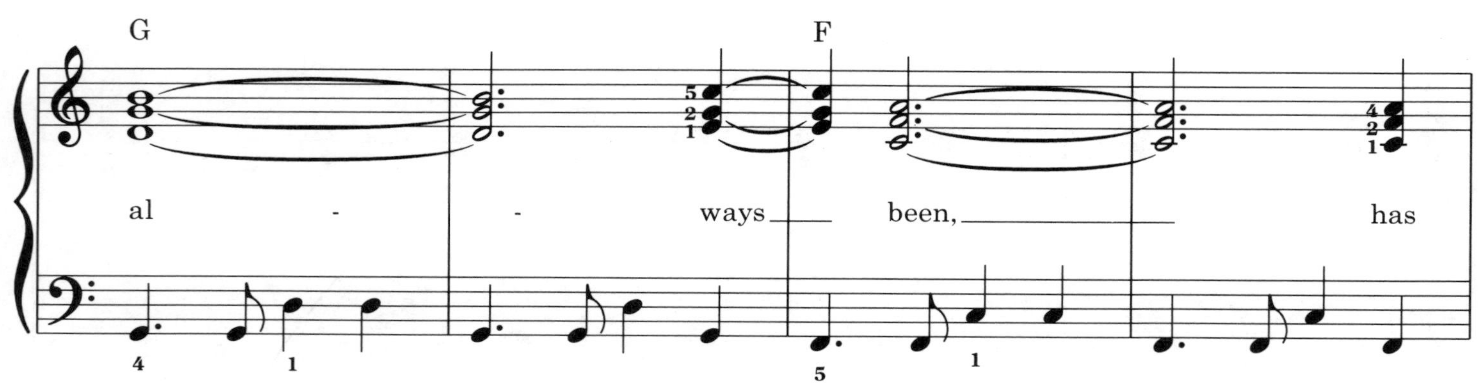
G
F
al - - ways
been,
has

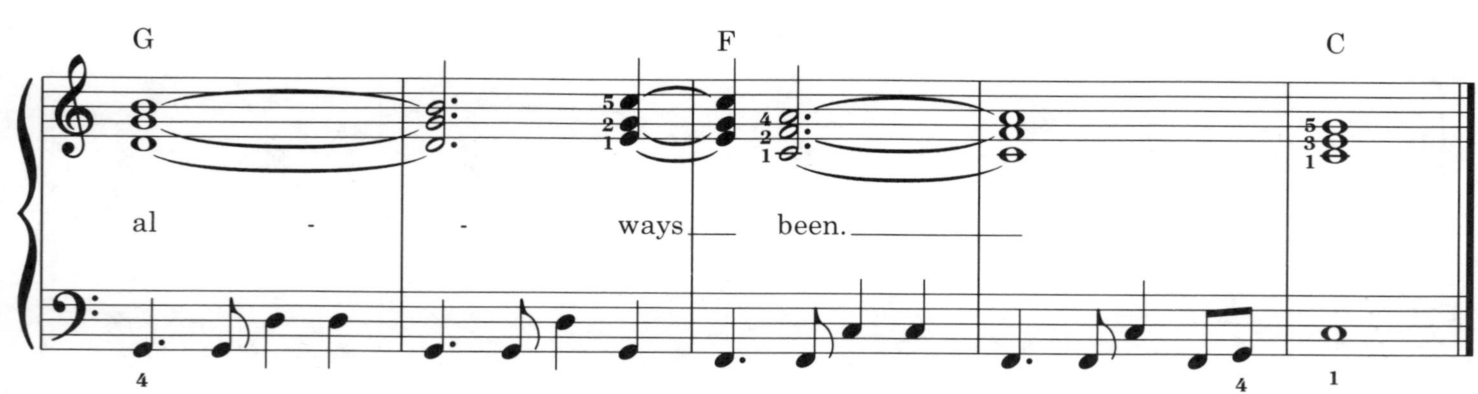
G
F
C
al - - ways
been.

DON'T IT MAKE MY BROWN EYES BLUE

Tempo 77
Voice 029
Style 056

Words and Music by
RICHARD LEIGH

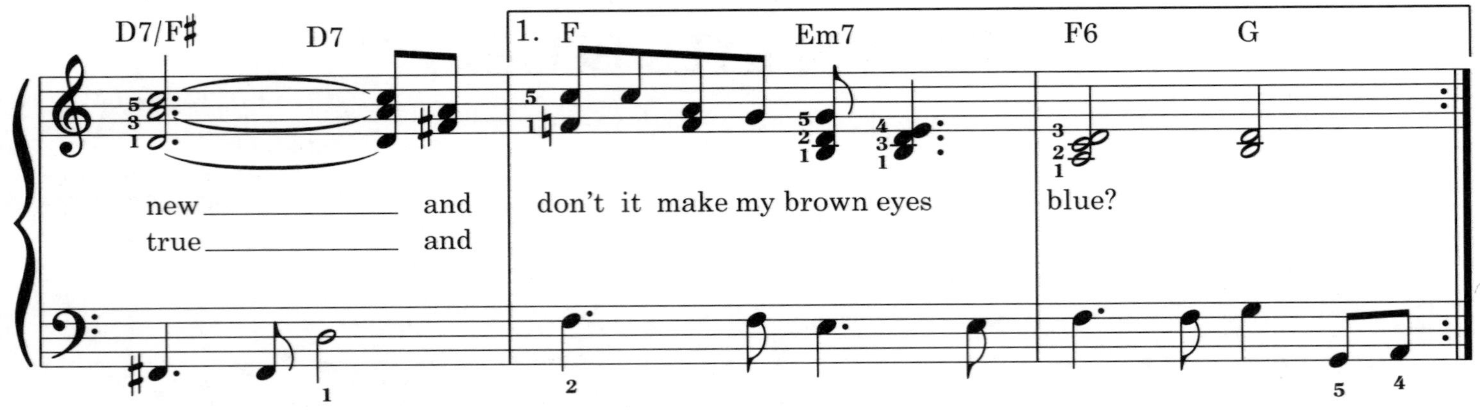
D7/F♯
D7
1. F
Em7
F6
G
new ___ and
true ___ and
don't it make my brown eyes
blue?

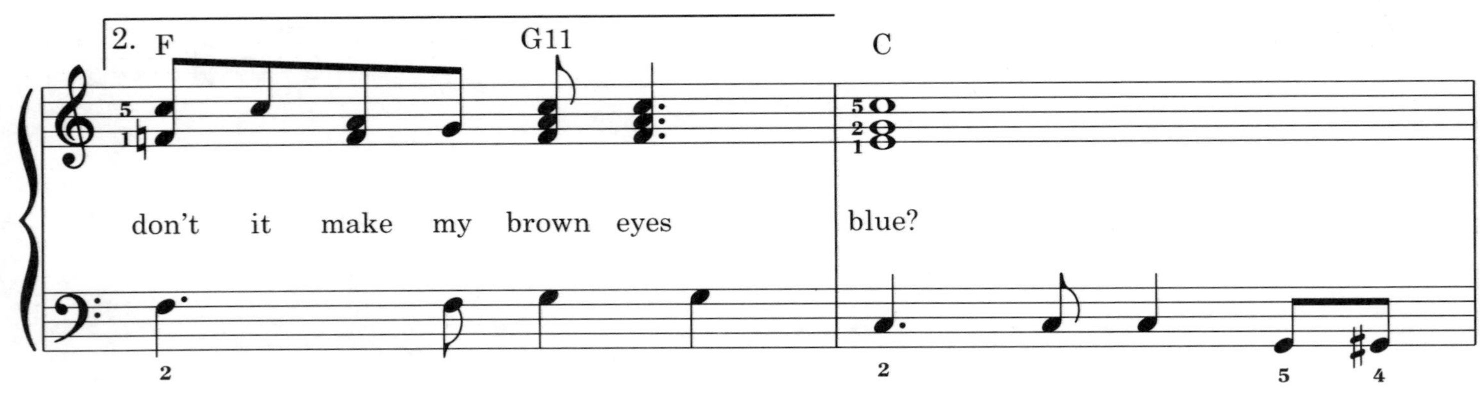
2. F
G11
C
don't it make my brown eyes
blue?

Am
Em7
F
C
Am
Em7
Tell me no se-crets,
tell me some lies,
give me no rea-sons, give me

F
C
Am
Em7
F
C
a - li - bis.
Tell me you love me and don't ___
let me cry, ___

Dm
Em
F
G11
C
Am
say a - ny-thing but
don't say good - bye.
I did - n't mean

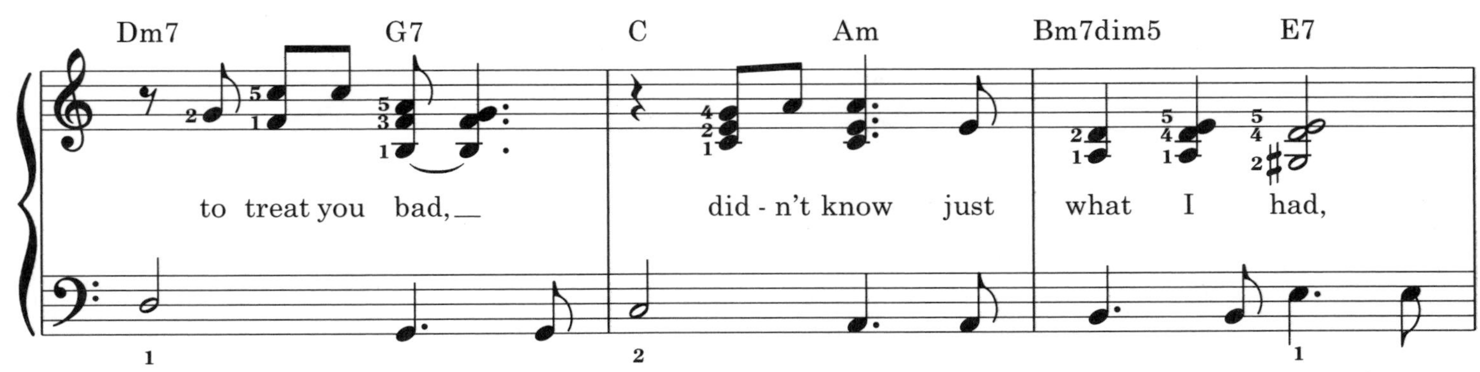
Dm7
G7
C
Am
Bm7dim5
E7
to treat you bad,
did - n't know just
what I had,

Am
C/G
D7/F♯
D7
F
Em7
but hon - ey now I
do, and
don't it make my brown eyes,

F
Em7
F
G11
C
don't it make my brown eyes,
don't it make my brown eyes
blue.

EAGLE WHEN SHE FLIES

Words and Music by
DOLLY PARTON

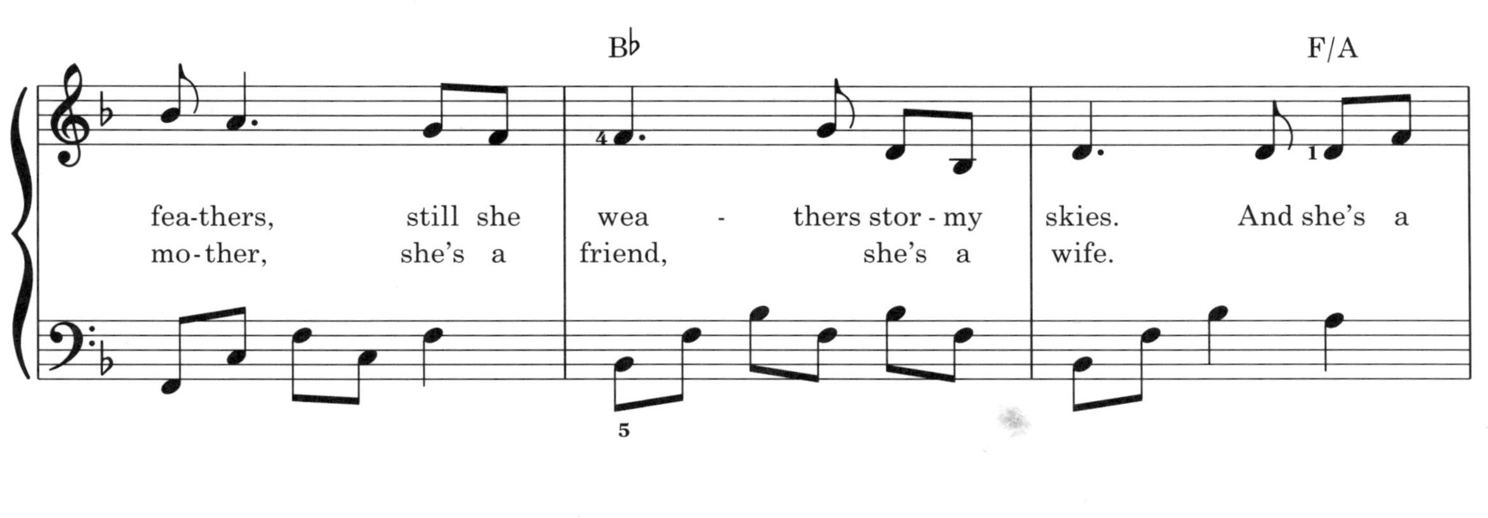
B♭
F/A
fea-thers, still she wea - thers stor-my skies. And she's a
mo-ther, she's a friend, she's a wife.

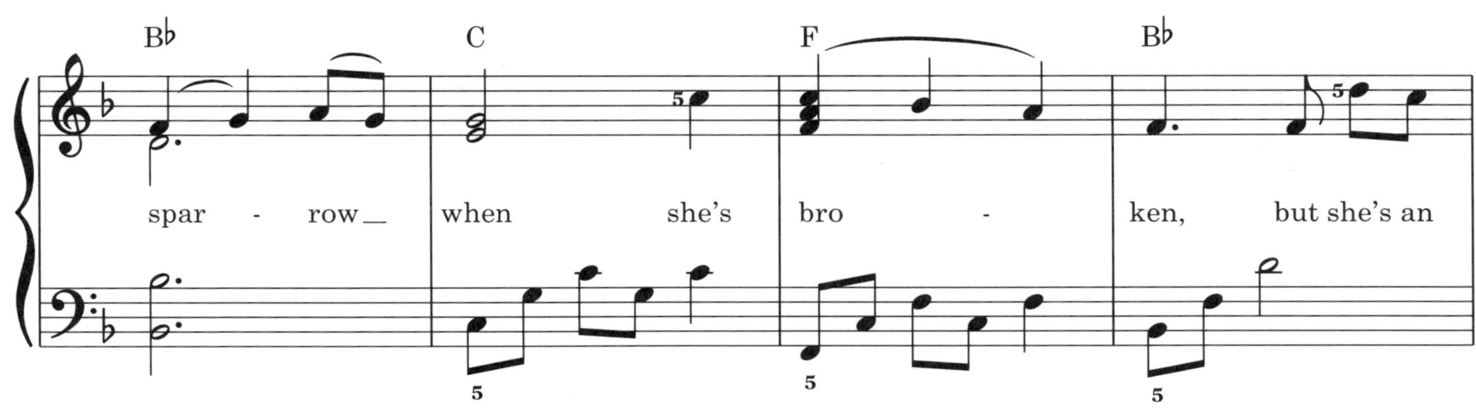
B♭
C
F
B♭
spar - row when she's bro - ken, but she's an

F
C
1.
F
C B♭/D C/E
ea - gle when she flies.
2. A Ka-

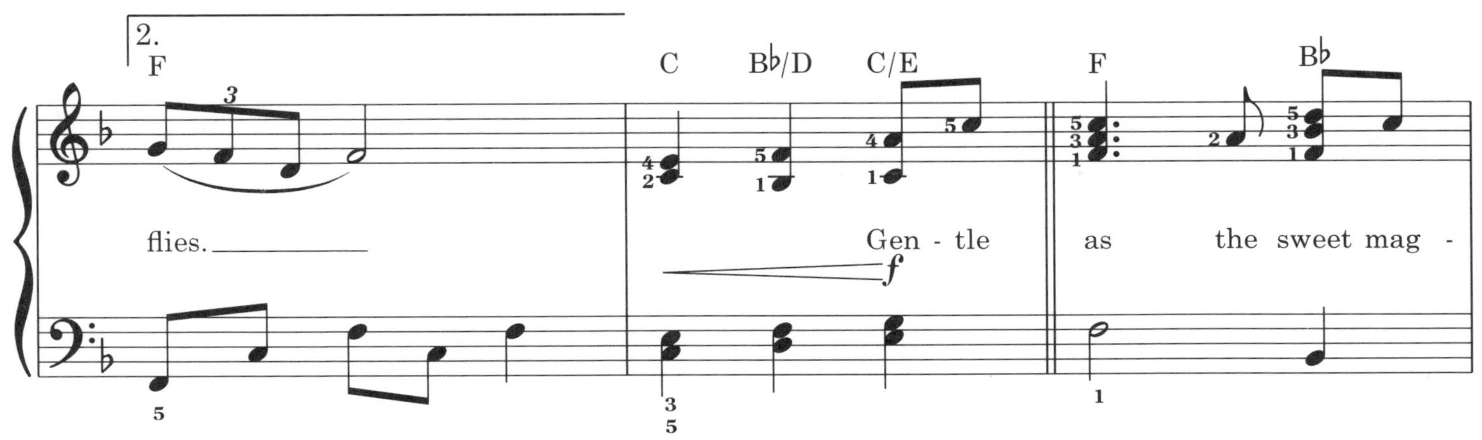
2.
F
C B♭/D C/E
F
B♭
flies.
Gen - tle as the sweet mag -
f

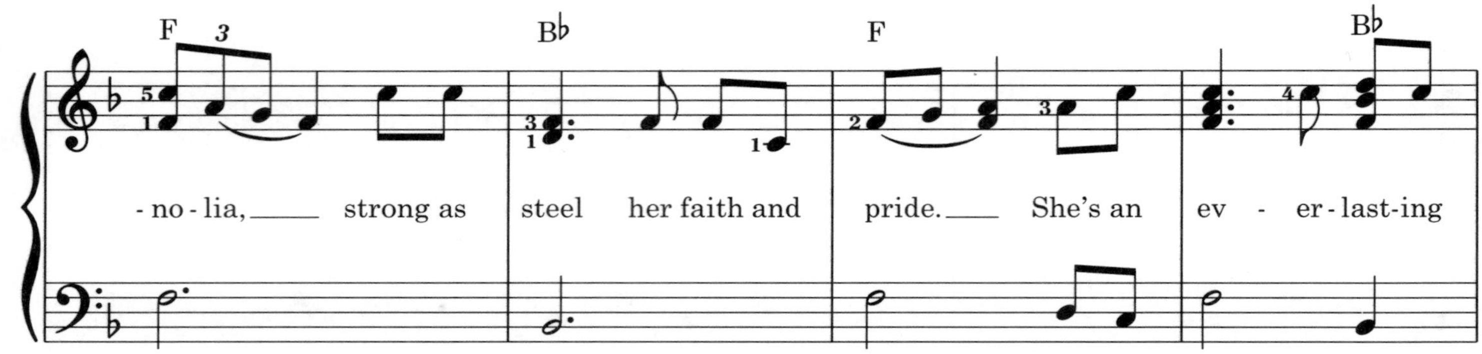
F
B♭
F
B♭
-no-lia, strong as steel her faith and pride. She's an ev - er-last-ing

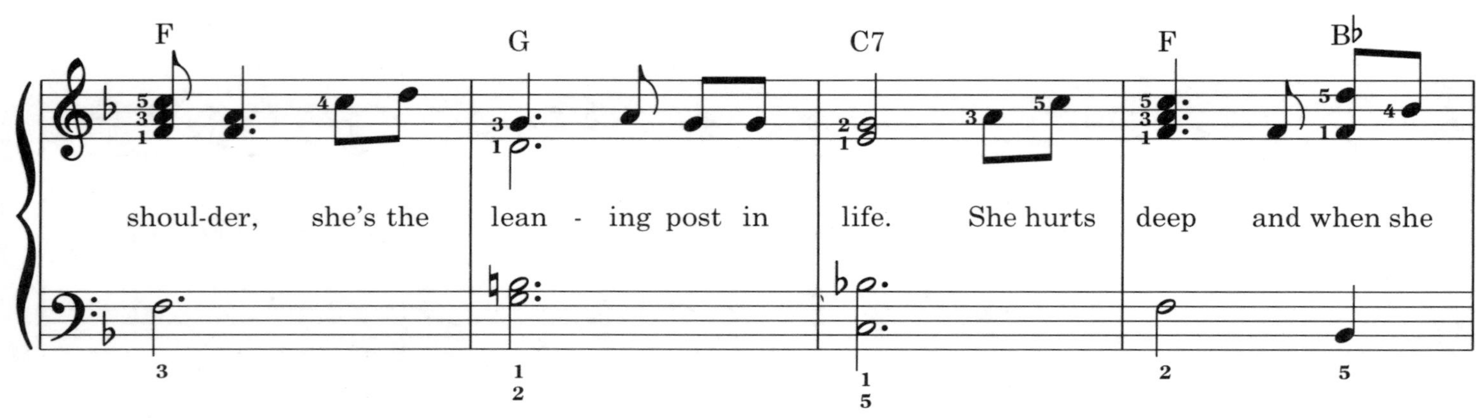
F
G
C7
F
B♭
shoul-der, she's the lean - ing post in life. She hurts deep and when she

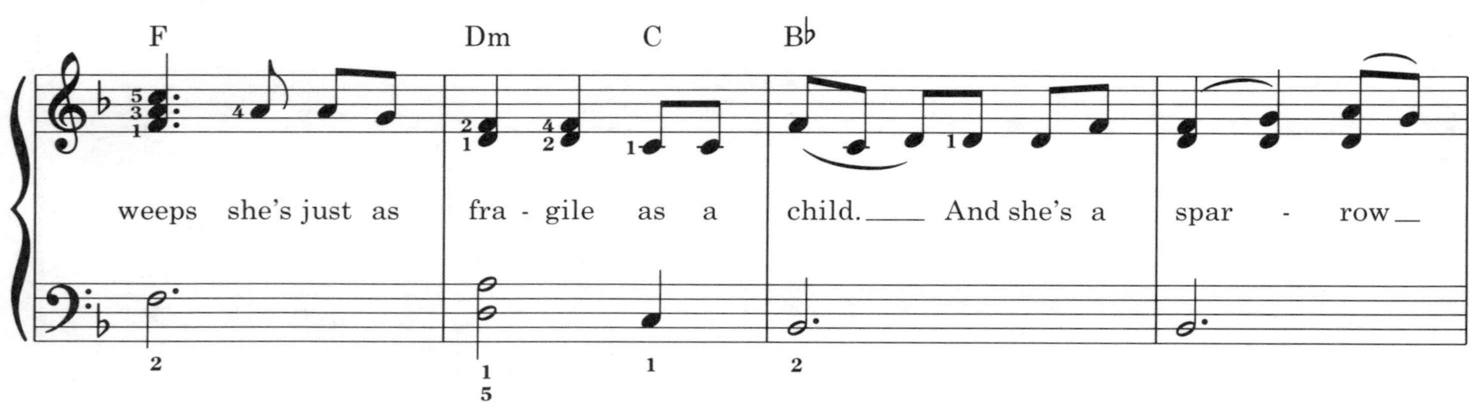
F
Dm
C
B♭
weeps she's just as fra - gile as a child. And she's a spar - row

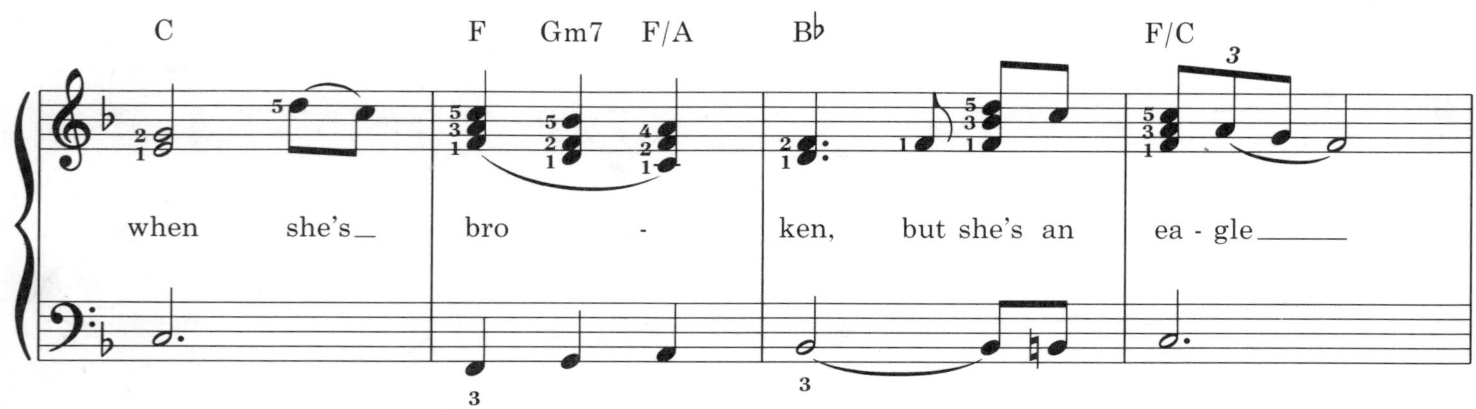
C
F
Gm7
F/A
B♭
F/C
when she's bro - ken, but she's an ea - gle

C7 F B♭ F/A B♭
when she flies. She's a spar - row

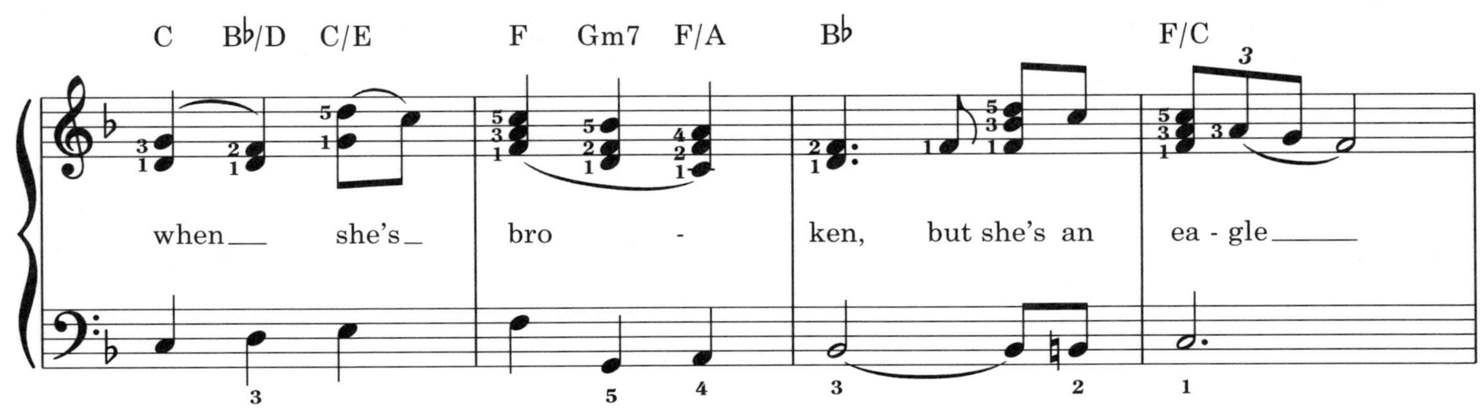
C B♭/D C/E F Gm7 F/A B♭ F/C
when she's bro - ken, but she's an ea - gle

B♭6/9 F F/A B♭ F/C
when she flies. Oh bless her Lord, she's an ea - gle

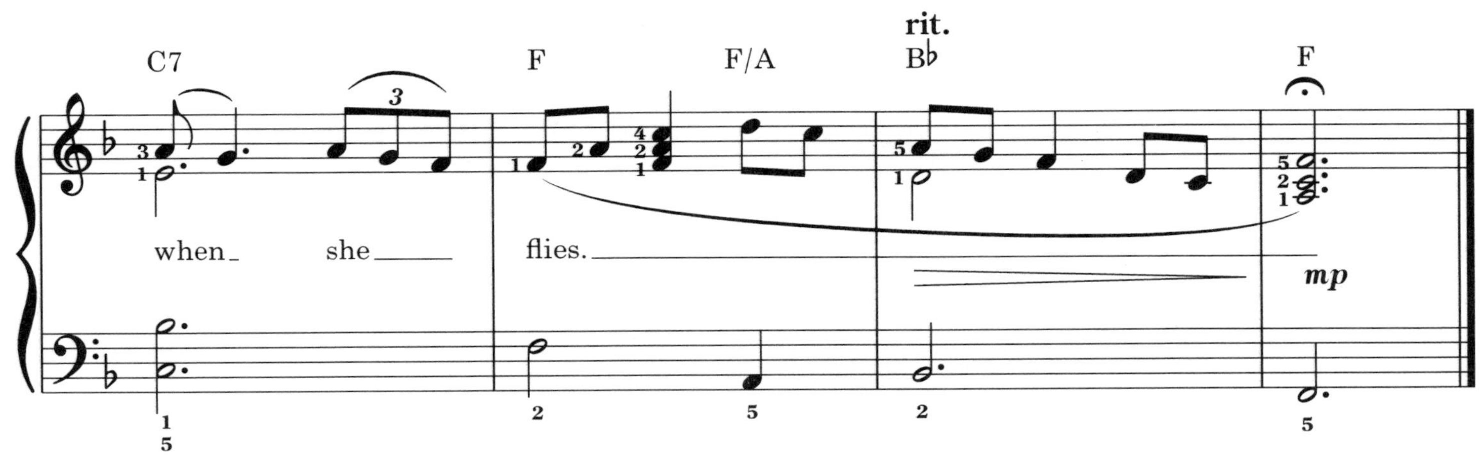
rit.
C7 F F/A B♭ F
when she flies.
mp

JOLENE

Words and Music by
DOLLY PARTON

F C Dm
-lene, Jo - lene, Jo - lene,
C Dm
please don't take him just be-cause you can.
F
Your beau - ty is be - yond com-pare, with
C Dm C
flam - ing locks of au - burn hair with iv - 'ry skin and eyes of em - 'rald
Dm
green. Your

Verse 2
He talks about you in his sleep
And there's nothing I can do to keep from crying
When he calls your name, Jolene
And I can eas'ly understand
How you could eas'ly take my man
But you don't know what he means to me, Jolene

Verse 3
You could have your choice of men
But I could never love again
He's the only one for me, Jolene
I had to have this talk with you
My happiness depends on you
And whatever you decide to do, Jolene

LIKE A SAD SONG

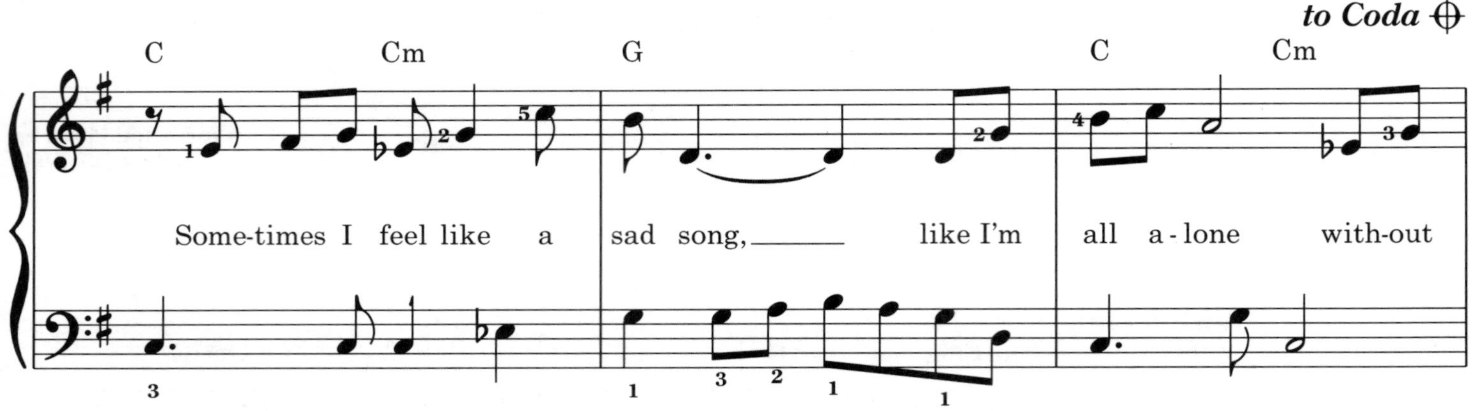
to Coda
C
Cm
G
C
Cm
Some-times I feel like a
sad song,
like I'm
all a-lone
with-out

1.
D
2.
D
C
Cm
you.
2. So
you.
I know that life goes on

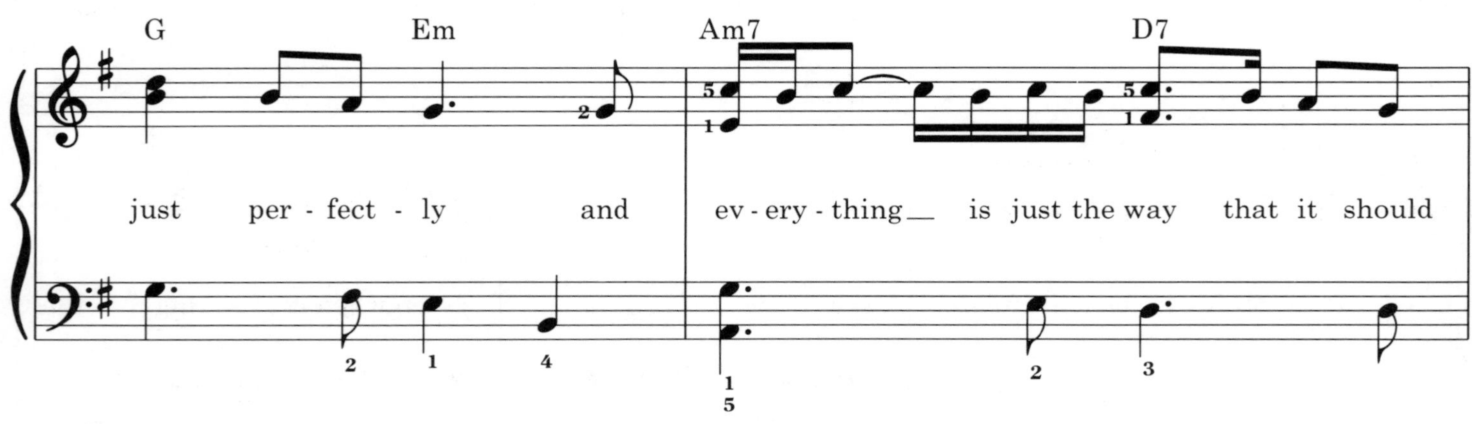
G
Em
Am7
D7
just per-fect-ly and
ev-ery-thing
is just the way that it should

G
C
Cm
G
Em
be.
Still there are times when my
heart feels like break-ing and

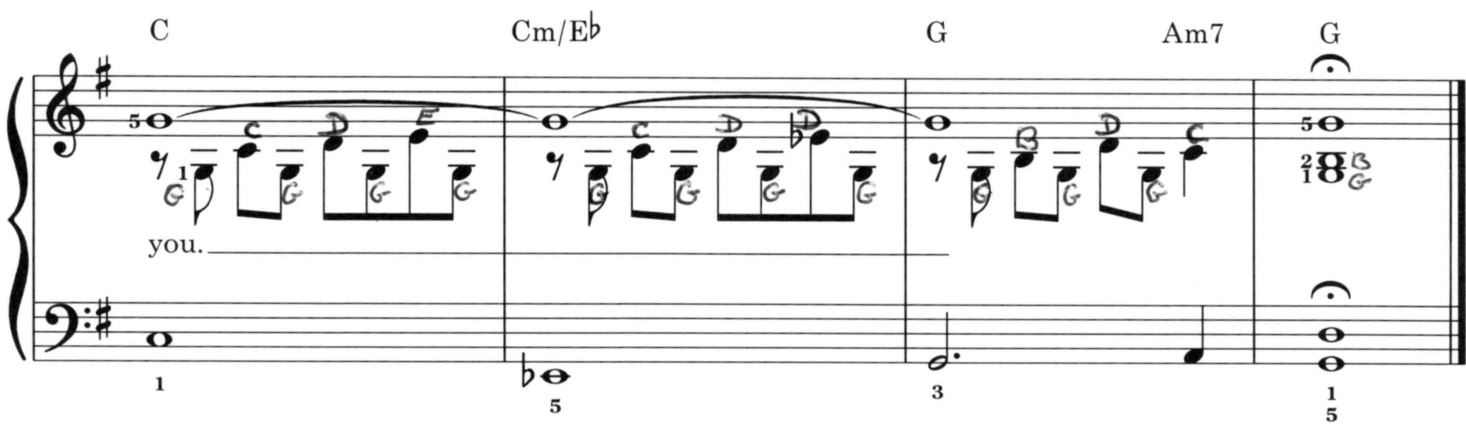

Verse 2
So many different places
A million smiling faces
Life is so incredible to me
Especially to be near you
And how it is to touch you
Oh paradise was made for you and me

Sometimes I feel like a sad song
Like I'm all alone without you

I know that life goes on just perfectly
And everything is just the way that it should be
Still there are times when my heart feels like breaking
And anywhere is where I'd rather be

Verse 3
Oh and in the night-time
I know that its the right time
To hold you close and say I love you so
To have someone to share with
And someone I can care with
And that is why I wanted you to know

LYIN' EYES

B-nova
Style 056
Voice 029
Tempo 077

Words and Music by
DON HENLEY and GLENN FREY

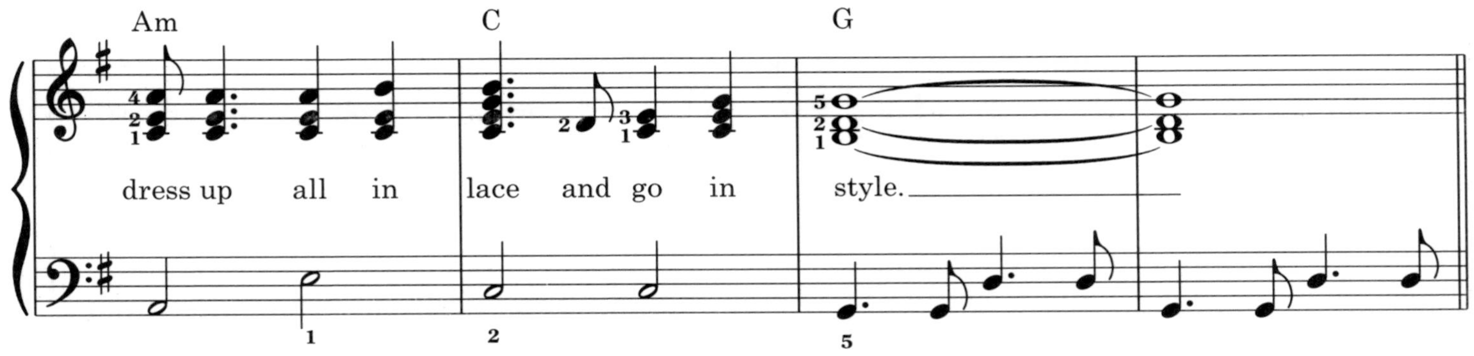
Am
C
G
dress up all in lace and go in style.

G
Gmaj7
C
Late at night a big old house gets lone - ly, I guess
tells him she must go out for the eve - ning, to

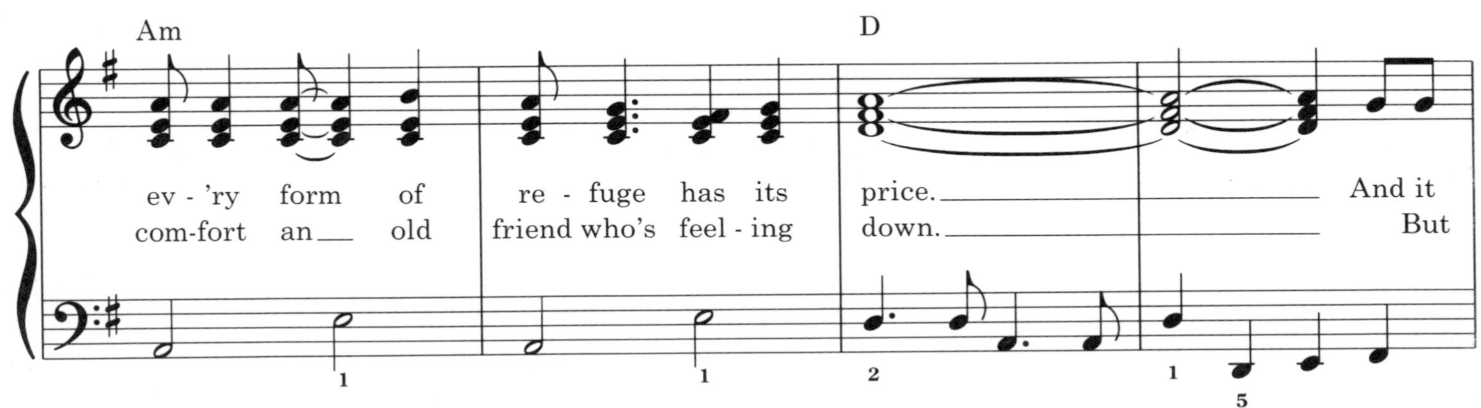
Am
D
ev - 'ry form of re - fuge has its price. And it
com-fort an old friend who's feel - ing down. But

G
Gmaj7
C
breaks her heart to think her love is on - ly giv-en
he knows where she's go - in' as she's leav - in', she is

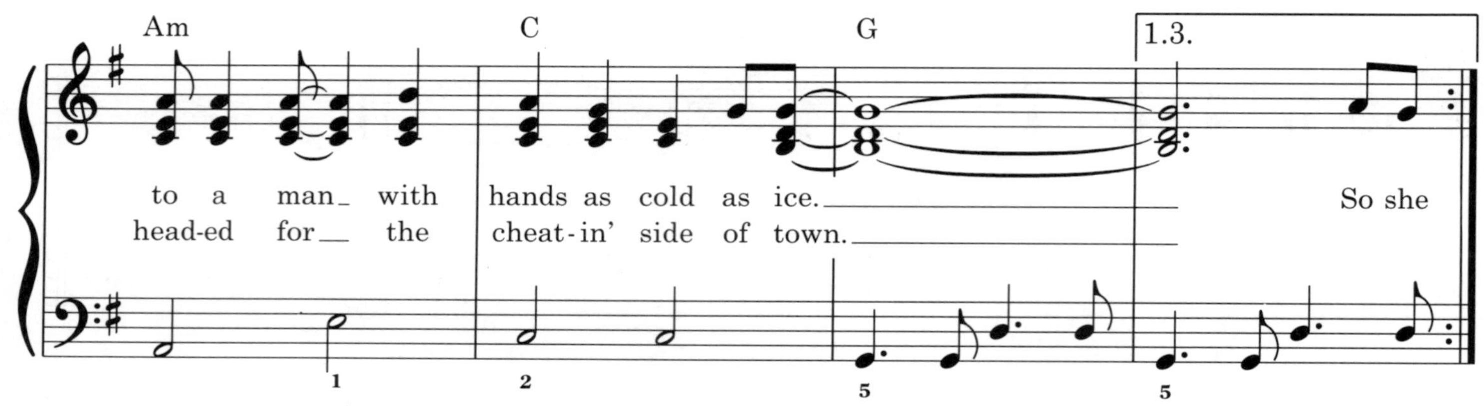
Am
C
G
1.3.
to a man_ with
hands as cold as ice.
So she
head-ed for__ the
cheat-in' side of town.

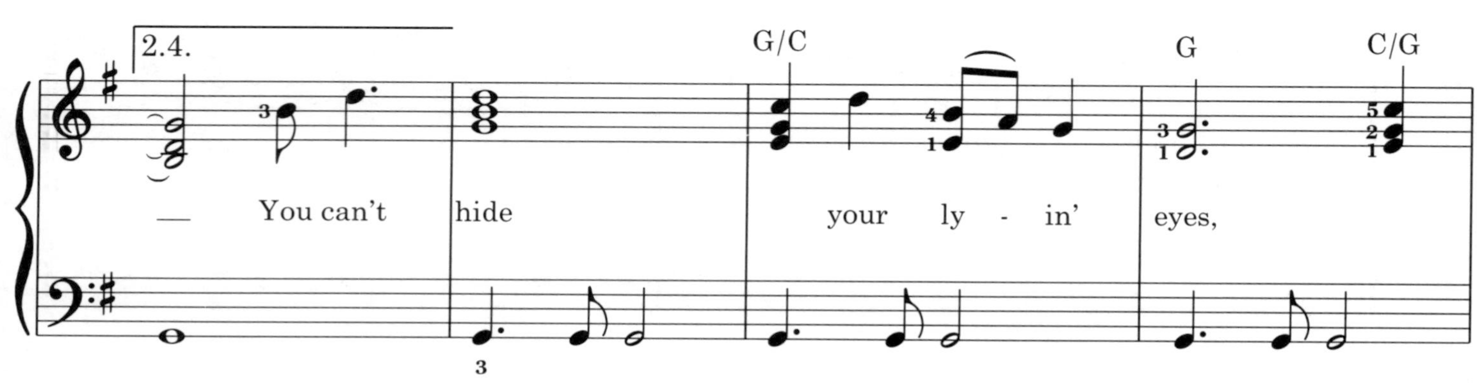
2.4.
G/C
G
C/G
You can't
hide
your ly - in'
eyes,

G
Em
Bm
Am
D
and your
smile
is a thin dis - guise
I thought by

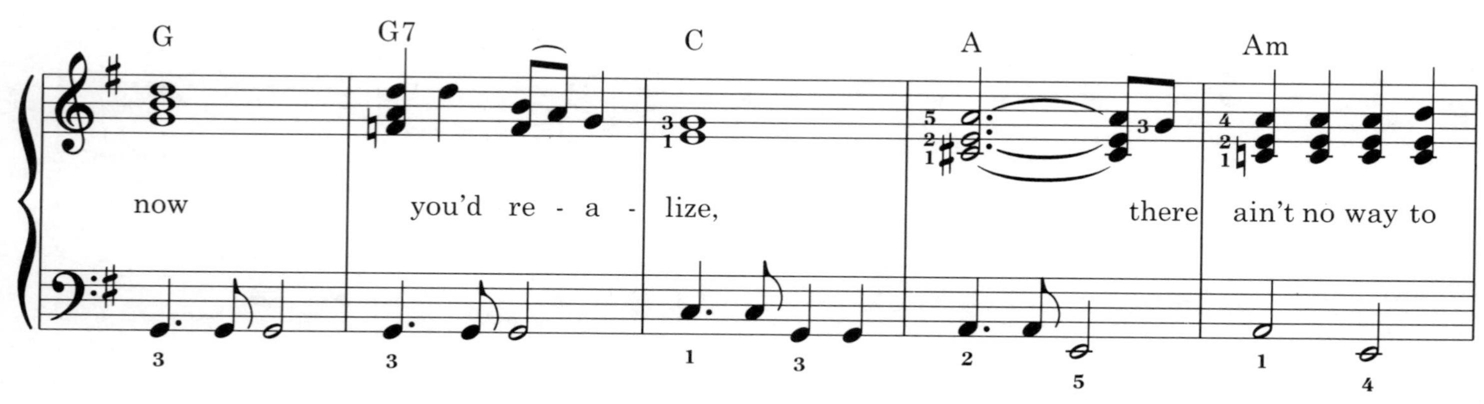
G
G7
C
A
Am
now
you'd re - a - lize,
there
ain't no way to

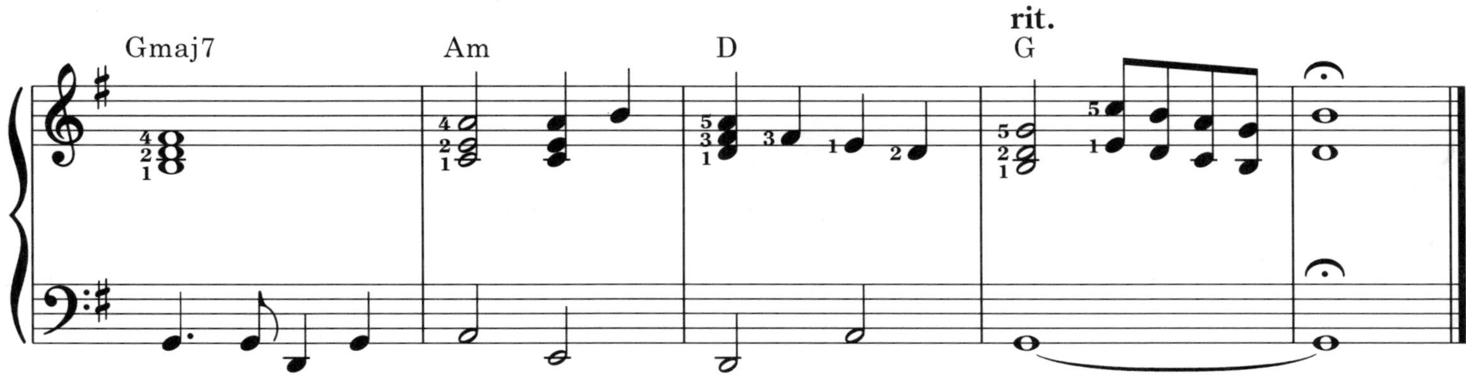

On the other side of town a boy is waiting
With fiery eyes and dreams no one could steal
She drives on through the night anticipating
'Cause he makes her feel the way she used to feel

She rushes to his arms, they fall together
She whispers that it's only for a while
She swears that soon she'll be comin' back for ever
She pulls away and leaves him with a smile

My oh my, you sure know how to arrange things
You set it up so well, so carefully
Ain't it funny how your new life didn't change things
You're still the same old girl you used to be

You can't hide your lyin' eyes
And your smile is a thin disguise
I thought by now you'd realize
There ain't no way to hide your lyin' eyes

OUTBOUND PLANE

Words and Music by
NANCI GRIFFITH and TOM RUSSELL

B♭sus4
A♭
E♭
B♭sus4
A♭
talk all night long, we may
ne - ver fi-gure out just
where love went wrong. And I
A♭
E♭/G
don't wan-na be stand-ing here and
I don't wan-na be talk - ing here. And
Fm7
B♭sus4
E♭
B♭sus4
I don't real-ly care who's to
blame, 'cause if
love won't fly on its own
to Coda
A♭
E♭/G
Fm7
B♭sus4
E♭
B♭add 4
free will, it's gon-na catch that out - bound
plane.
A♭add 9
B♭add 4
E♭
B♭add 4
A♭add 9
B♭add 4

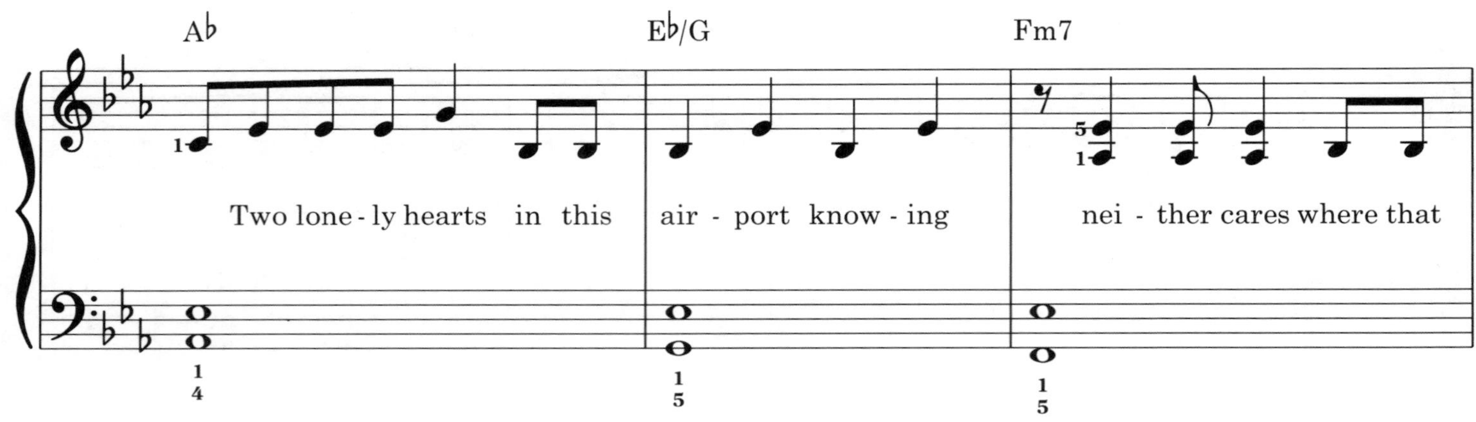
A♭
E♭/G
Fm7
Two lone - ly hearts in this air - port know - ing nei - ther cares where that

B♭7sus4
E♭
B♭sus4
A♭
E♭/G
oth-er heart is go-ing, but if love won't fly on its own free will, it's gon-na catch

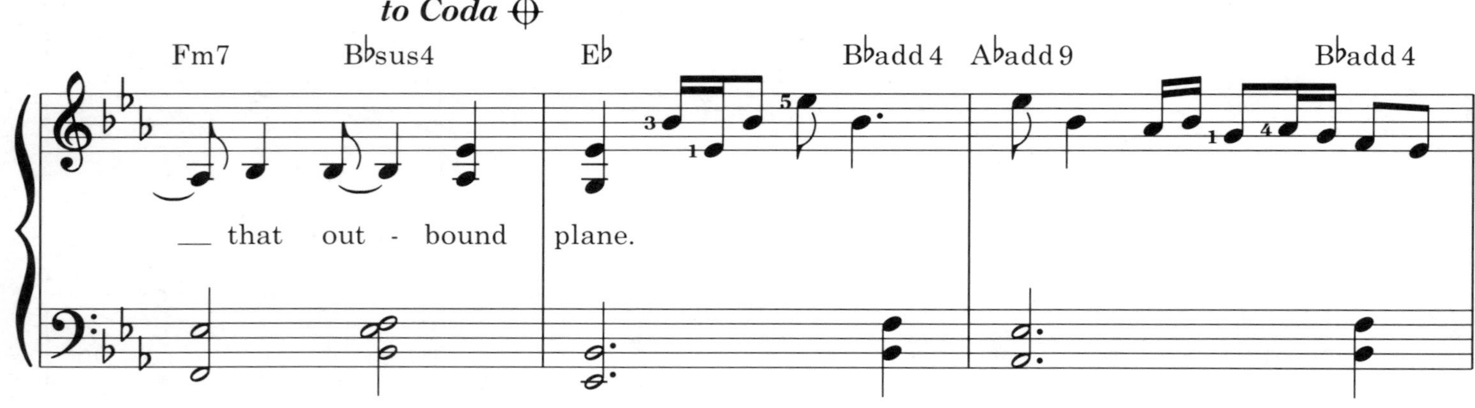
to Coda
Fm7
B♭sus4
E♭
B♭add 4
A♭add 9
B♭add 4
that out - bound plane.

D.S. al Coda
CODA
E♭
B♭add 4
A♭add 9
B♭add 4
E♭
B♭add 4
plane. If

Verse 2
The old folks say love is not forever anymore
Because these young people walk away from love, alone to pace the floor
Young or old, I say that love is still the same
And you may walk away from love, but you'll fall head and heel again

Verse 3
That frown you're wearing's just your halo turned upside down
Where is the laughter we once shared back in the lost and found
These broken wings are gonna leave me here to stand my ground
And you may have this ticket for that lonely plane that's flying out

STANDING OUTSIDE THE FIRE

Words and Music by
JENNY YATES and GARTH BROOKS

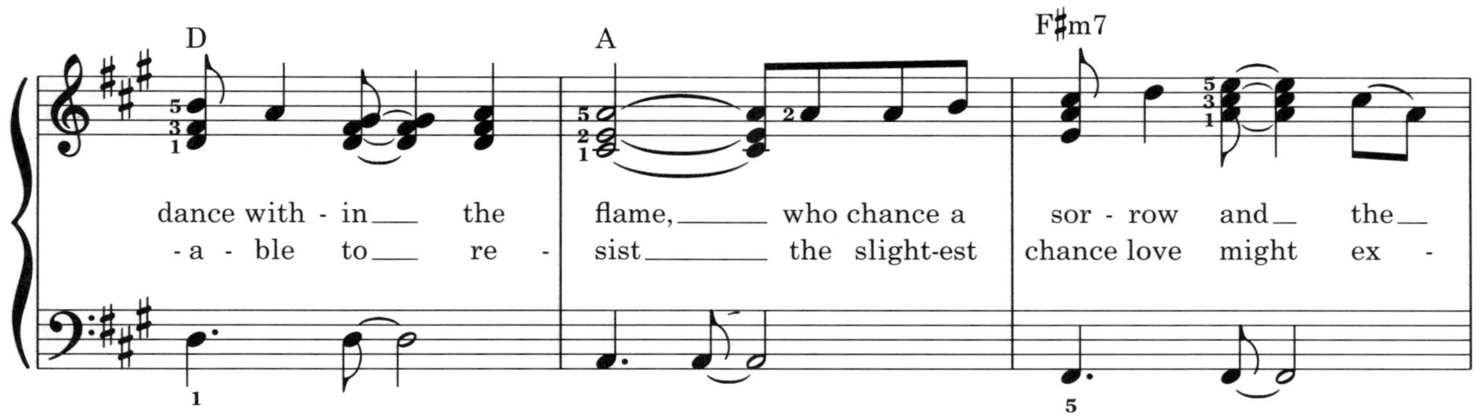
D
A
F♯m7
dance with - in ___ the flame, ___ who chance a sor - row and ___ the ___
- a - ble to ___ re - sist ___ the slight-est chance love might ex -

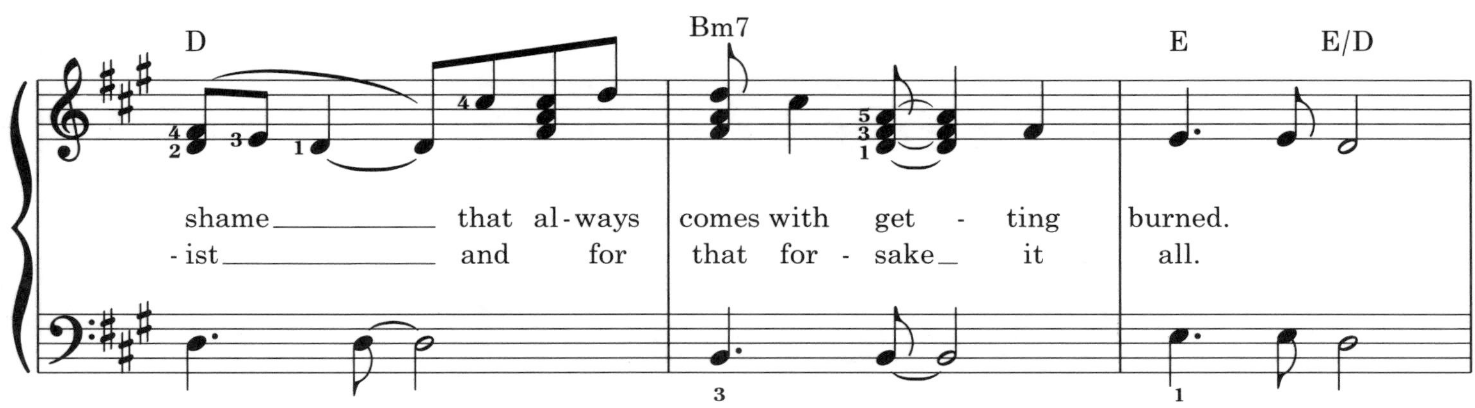
D
Bm7
E
E/D
shame ___ that al-ways comes with get - ting burned.
- ist ___ and for that for - sake ___ it all.

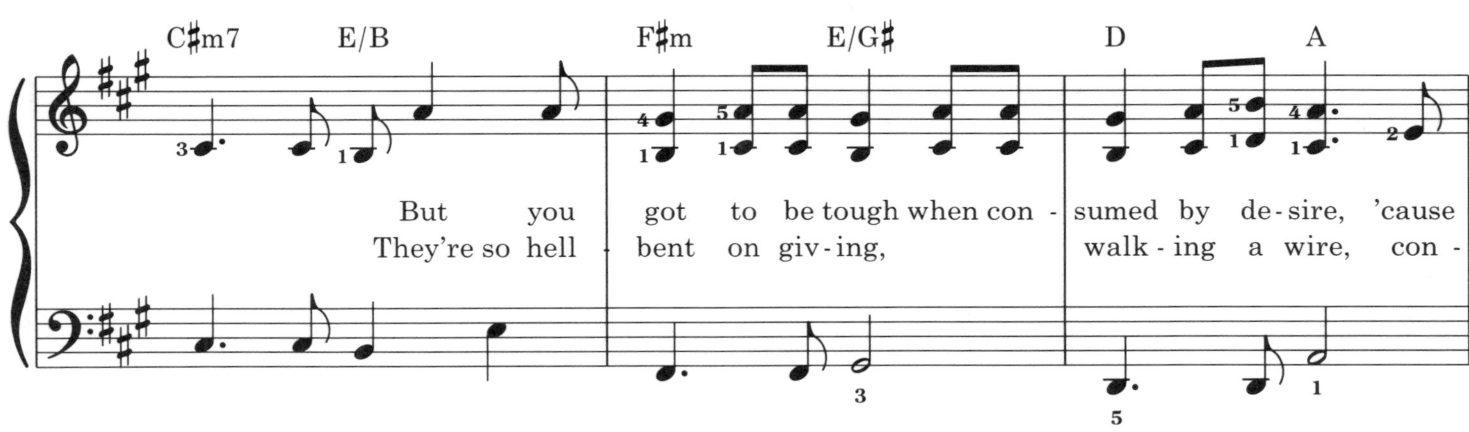
C♯m7
E/B
F♯m
E/G♯
D
A
But you got to be tough when con - sumed by de-sire, 'cause
They're so hell - bent on giv-ing, walk - ing a wire, con -

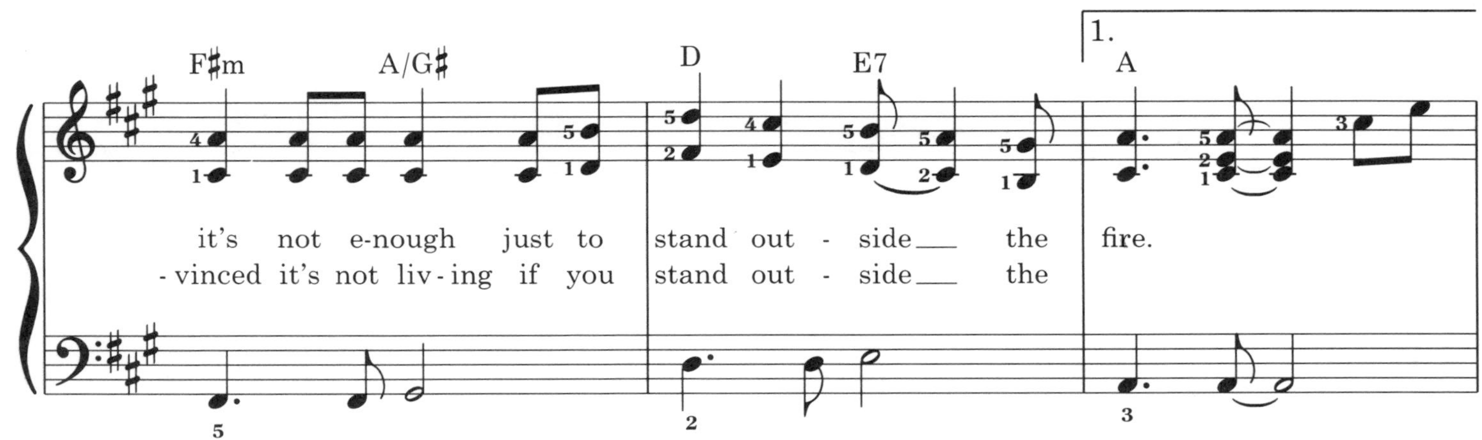
F♯m
A/G♯
D
E7
1.
A
it's not e-nough just to stand out - side ___ the fire.
- vinced it's not liv-ing if you stand out - side ___ the

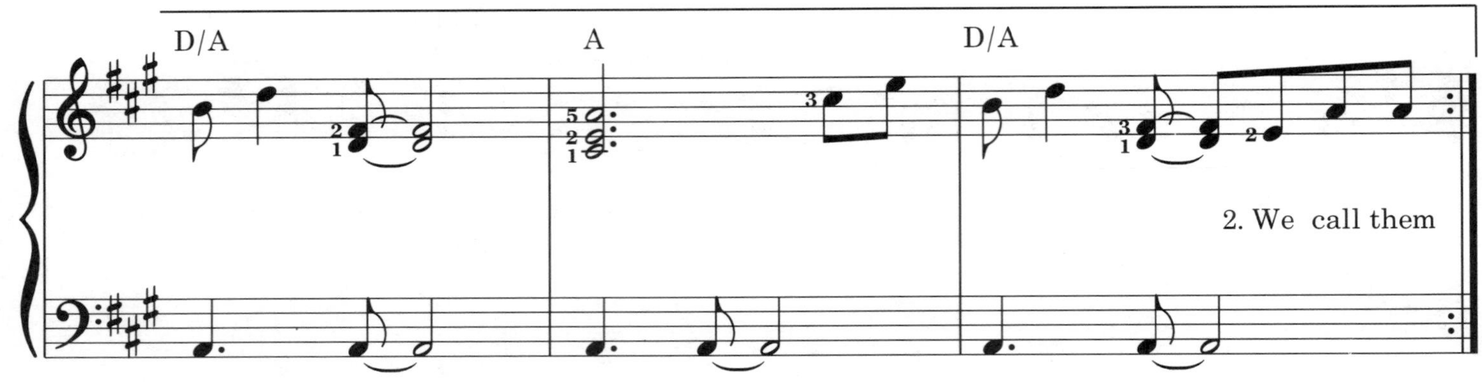
D/A
A
D/A
2. We call them

2. A
D
Esus4
fire.
Stand-ing out-side the

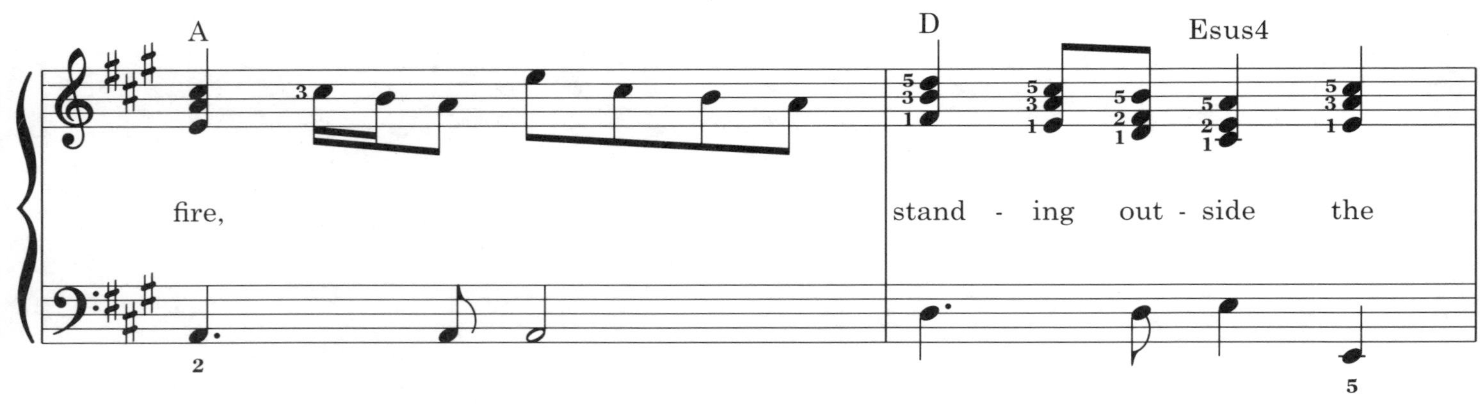
A
D
Esus4
fire,
stand - ing out - side the

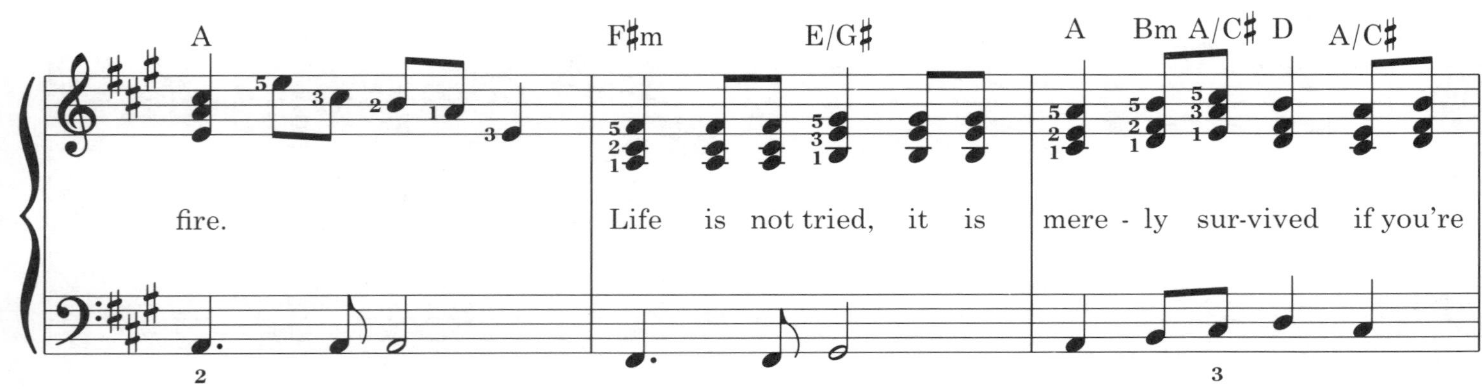
A
F♯m
E/G♯
A
Bm
A/C♯
D
A/C♯
fire.
Life is not tried, it is
mere - ly sur-vived if you're

Bm
Esus4
A
stand - ing out-side the
fire.
There's this

D
A/C♯
Bm
love that is burn-ing
deep in my soul,_
con - stant-ly yearn-ing to get

A
D
A/C♯
out of con - trol,_
want - ing to fly___
high - er and high-er,

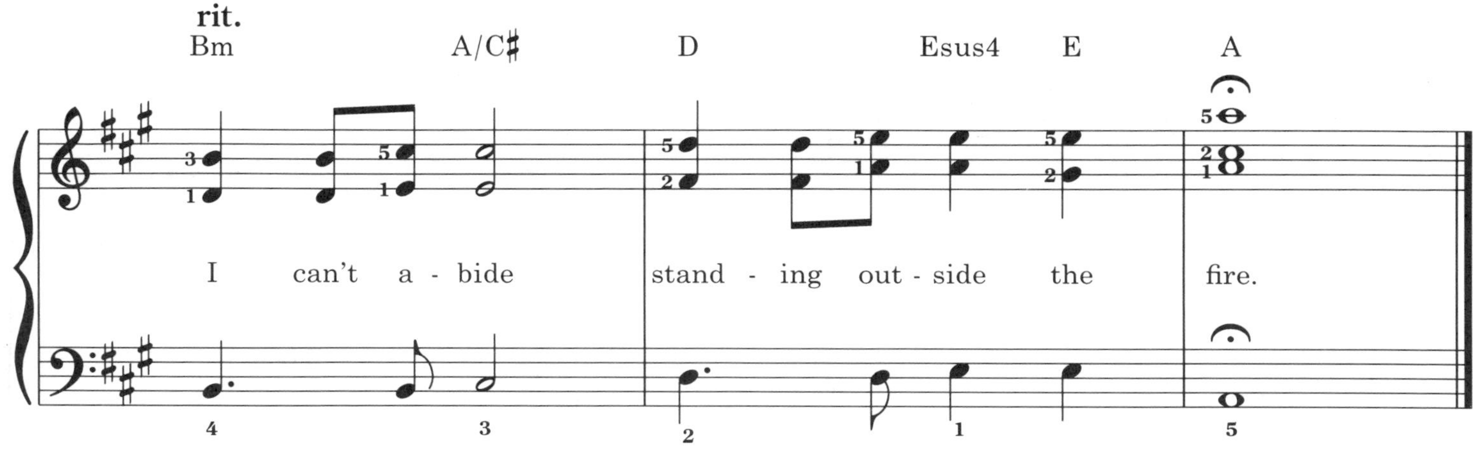
rit.
Bm
A/C♯
D
Esus4
E
A
I can't a - bide
stand - ing out - side the
fire.

TAKE IT TO THE LIMIT

Words and Music by
RANDY MEISNER, DON HENLEY and GLENN FREY

Moderately with a swing

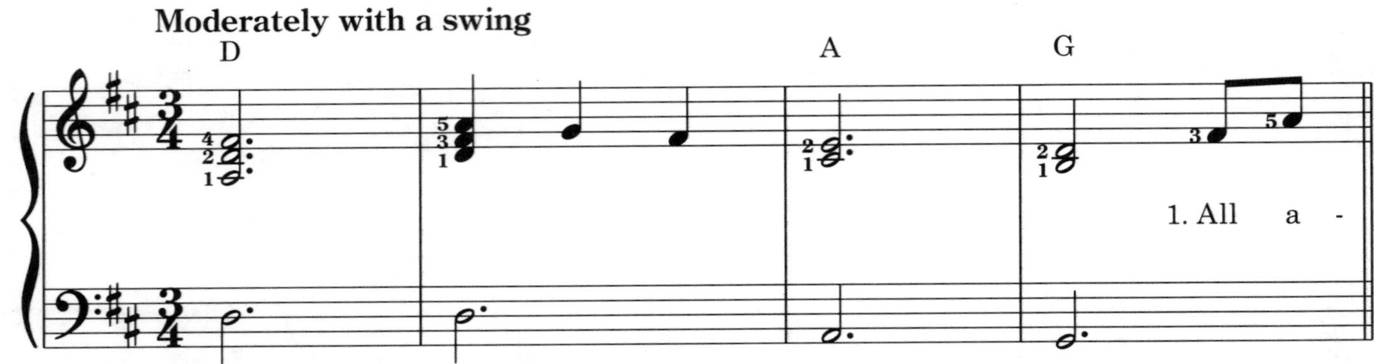

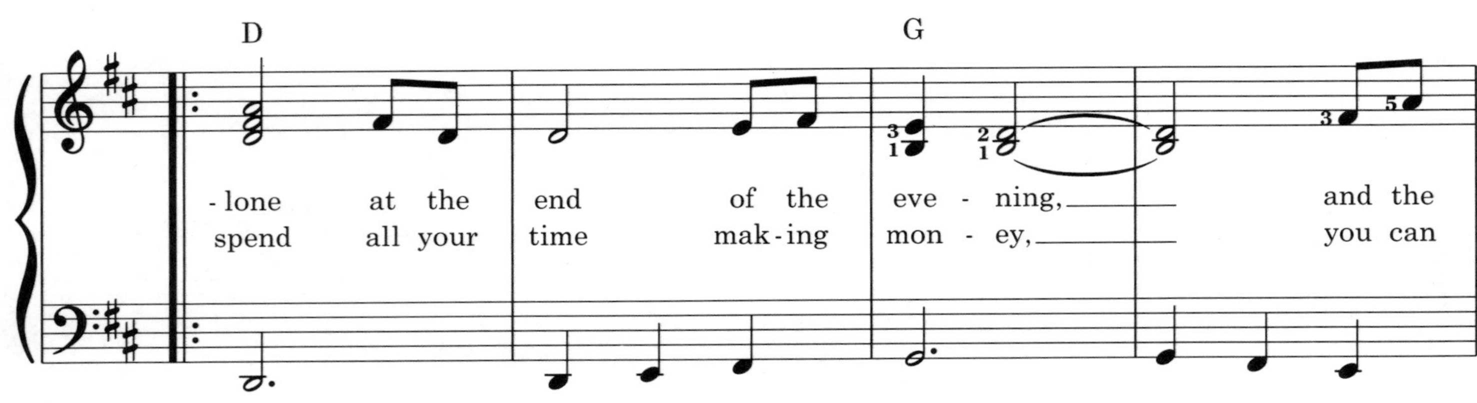

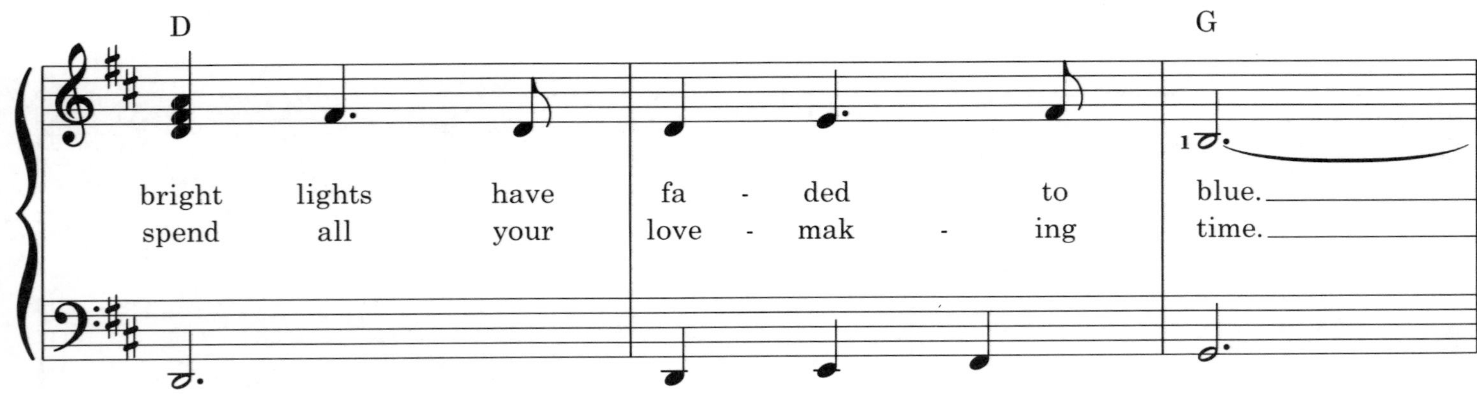

D
F♯
I was thinking-ing 'bout a wo-man who might have
If it all fell to pie-ces to-

Bm
A
A/G
loved me and I ne-ver knew.
-mor-row, would you still be mine?

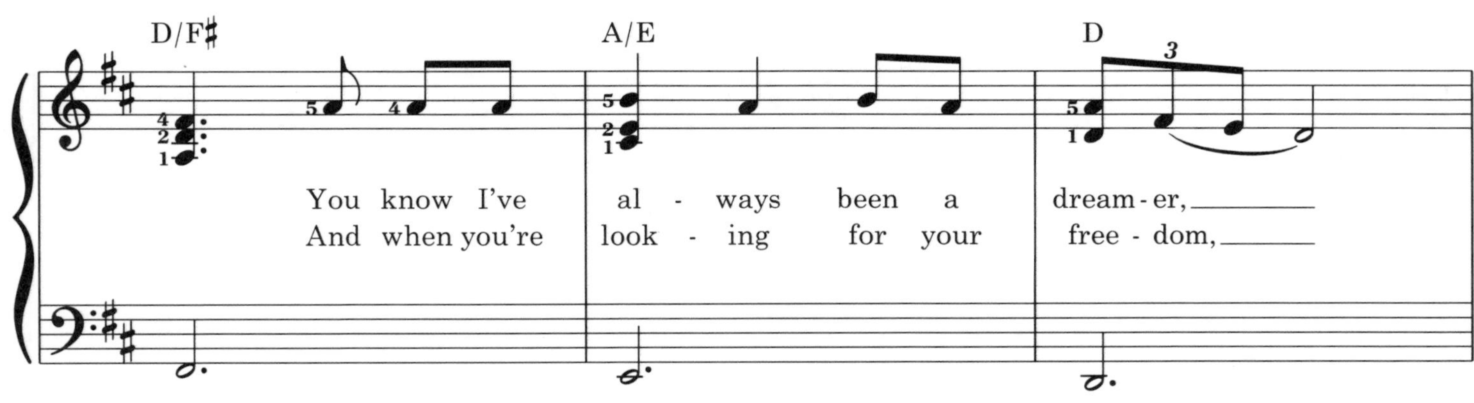
D/F♯
A/E
D
You know I've al-ways been a dream-er,
And when you're look-ing for your free-dom,

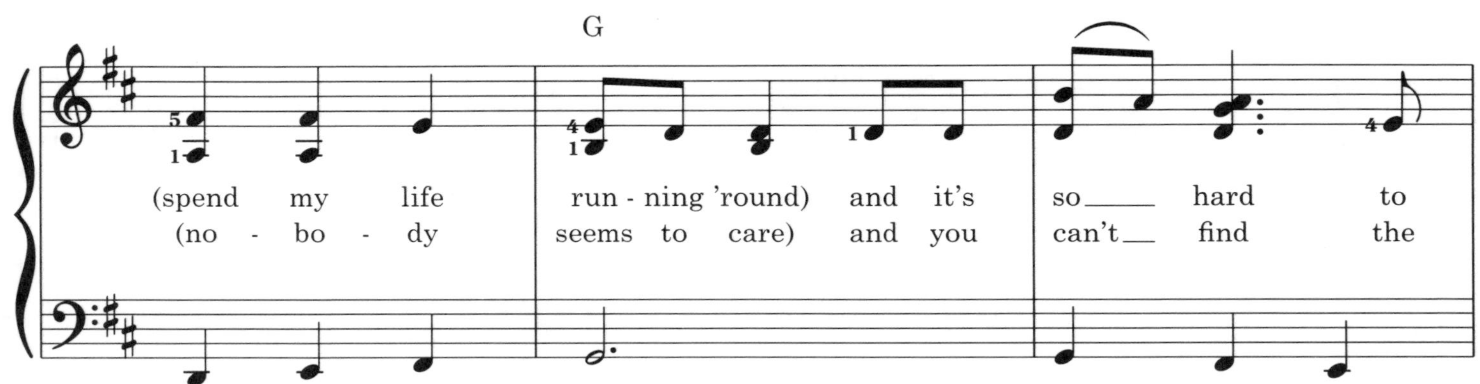
G
(spend my life run-ning 'round) and it's so hard to
(no-bo-dy seems to care) and you can't find the

D
G
change
(can't seem to
set - tle down) but the
door,
(can't find it
a - ny - where) when there's

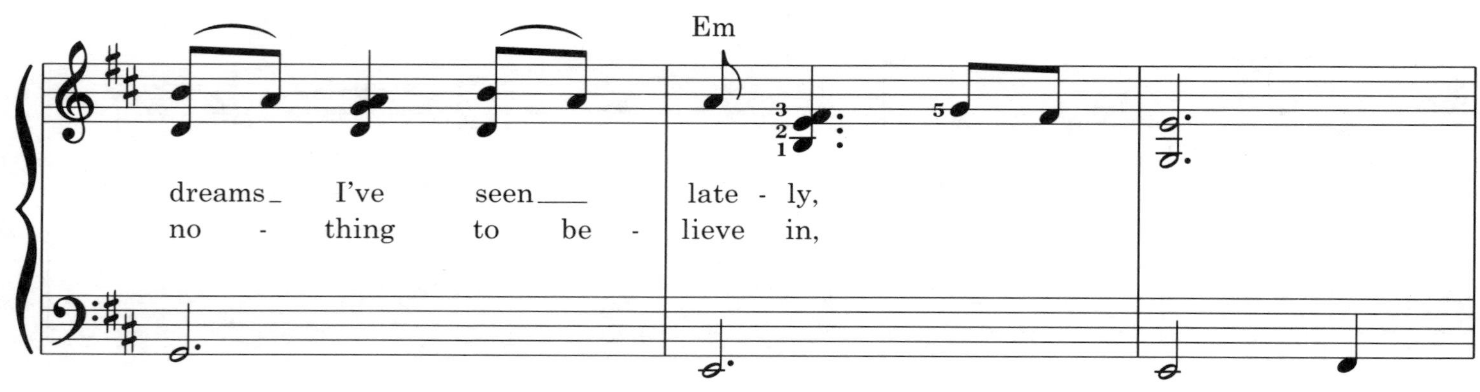
Em
dreams I've seen
late - ly,
no - thing to be -
lieve in,

G
A11
keep on
turn - ing out and
burn - ing out and
still you're
com - ing back, you're
run - ning back, you're

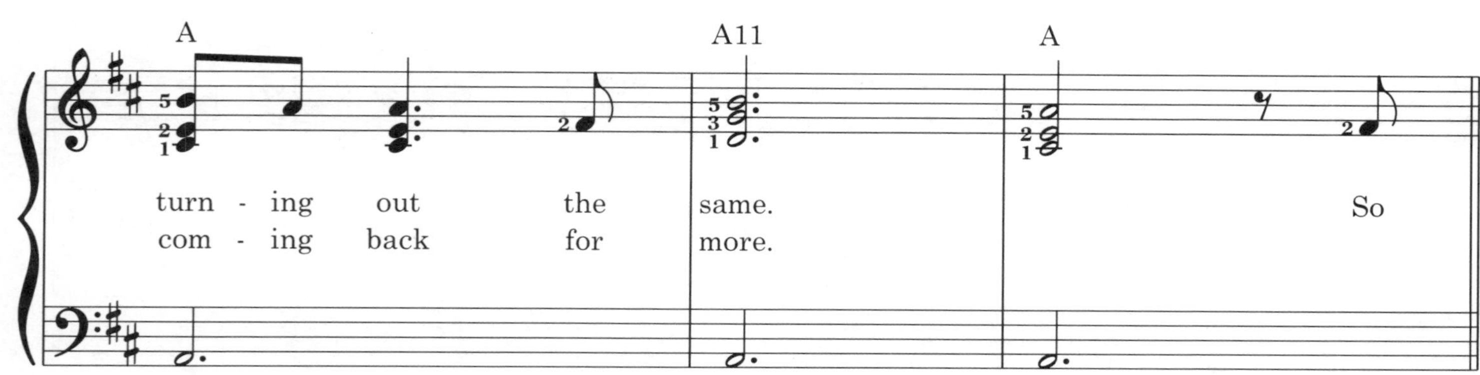
A
A11
A
turn - ing out the
same.
So
com - ing back for
more.

G
D
3
G
5
3
1
5
put me on a high - way and show me a

D
G
N.C.
A
4
1
1
3
2
5
5
2
1
4
sign, and take it to the li - mit, one more

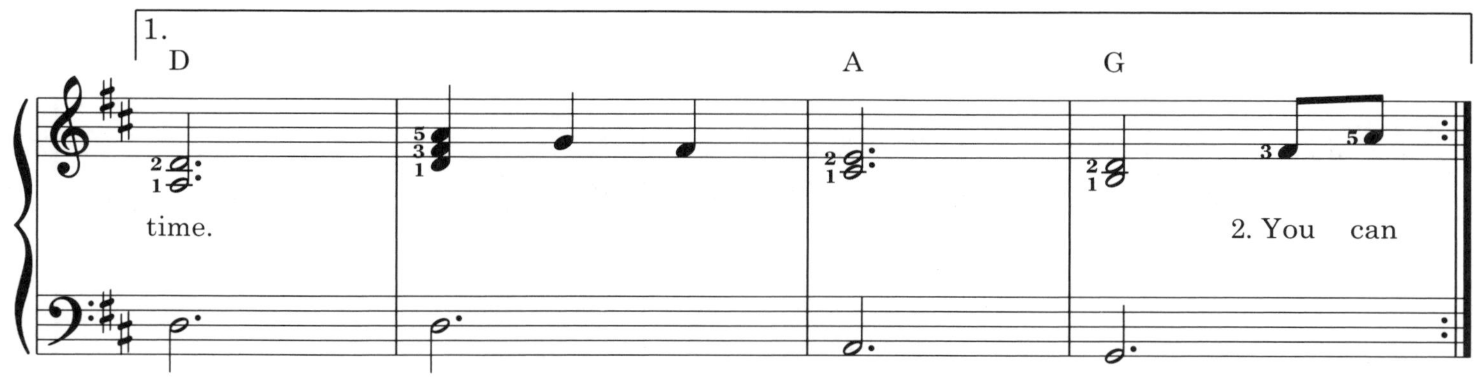
1.
D
A
G
2
1
5
3
1
2
1
2
1
3
5
time.
2. You can

2.
rit.
Bm
G
A
D
3
1
5
2
1
5
3
1
5
3
1
time.

TAKE ME HOME, COUNTRY ROADS

Words and Music by BILL DANOFF,
TAFFY NIVERT and JOHN DENVER

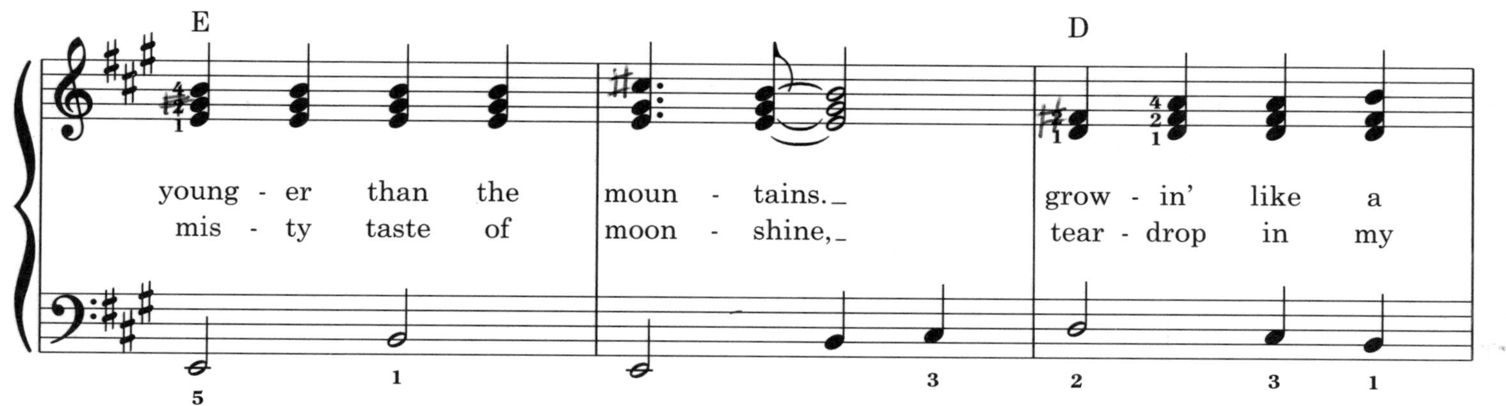
E
D
young - er than the moun - tains. grow - in' like a
mis - ty taste of moon - shine, tear - drop in my
5 1 3 2 3 1

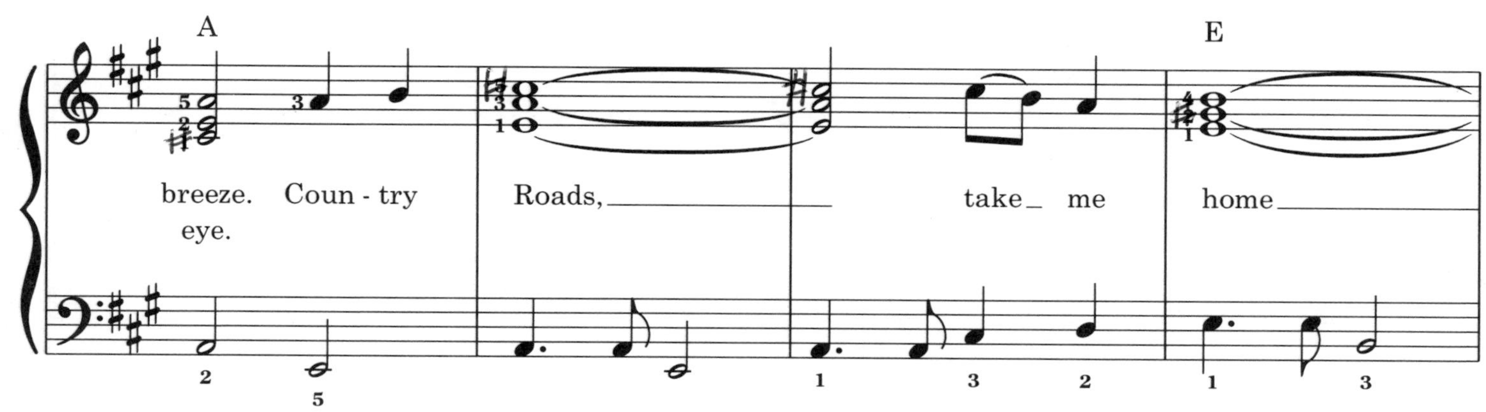
A
E
breeze. Coun - try Roads, take me home
eye.
2 5 1 3 2 1 3

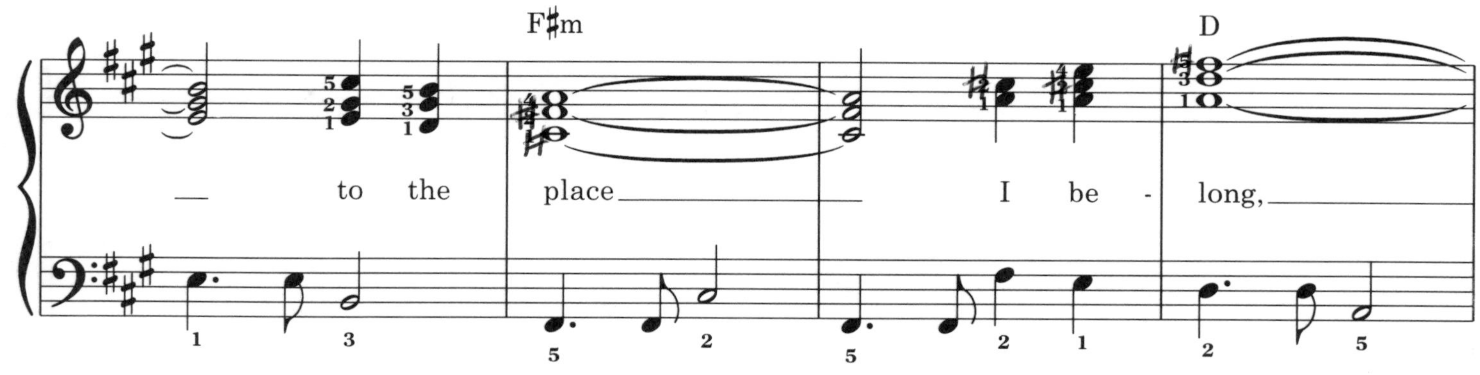
F♯m
D
to the place I be - long,
1 3 5 2 5 2 1 2 5

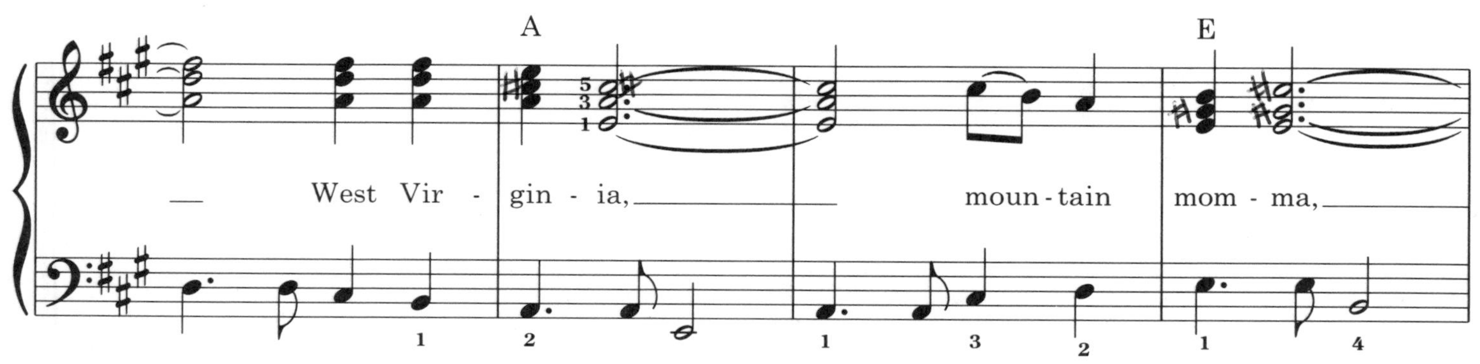
A
E
West Vir - gin - ia, moun - tain mom - ma,
1 2 1 3 2 1 4

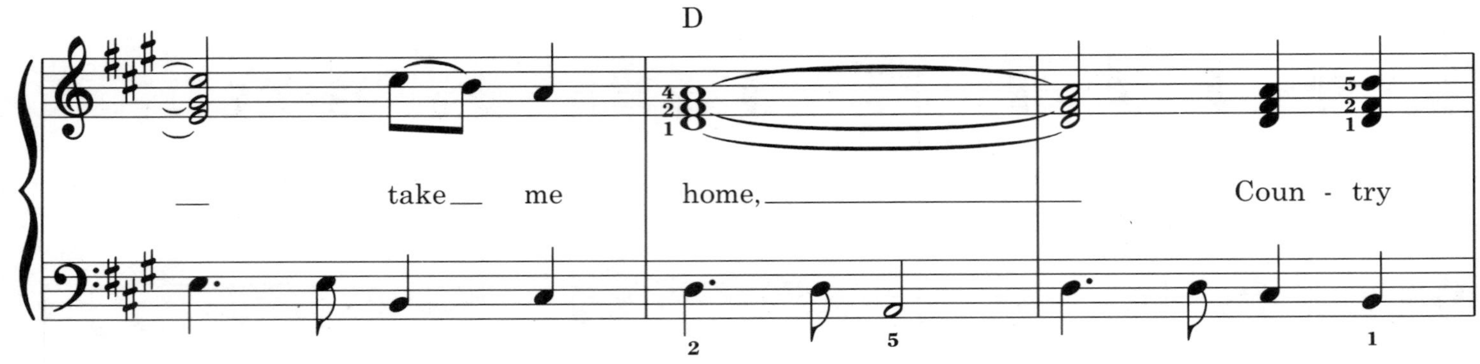
D
— take — me
home, —
Coun - try

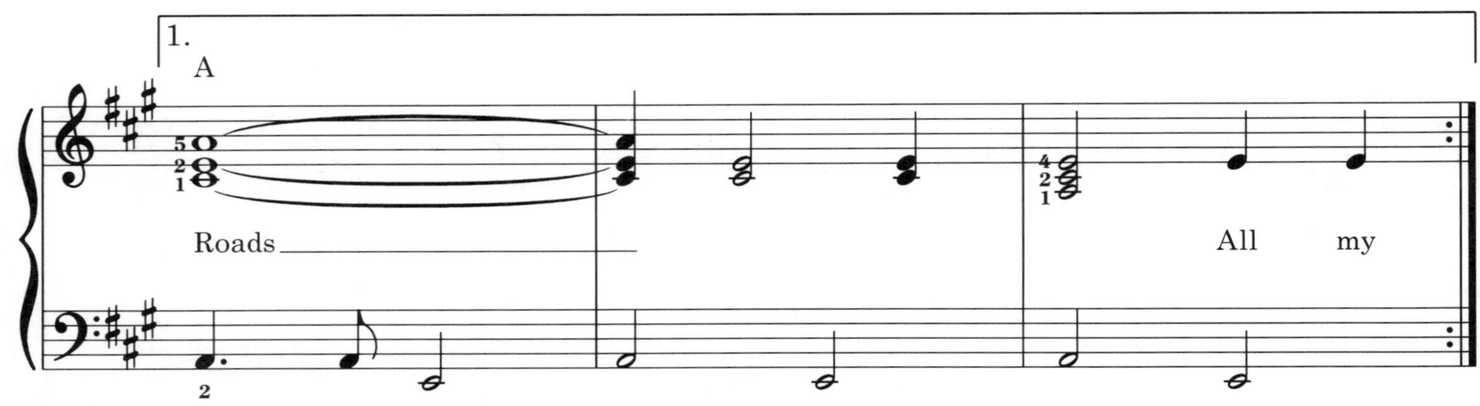
1.
A
Roads —
All my

2.
A
E
Roads —
take — me
home, —

rit.
A
— Coun - try
Roads.

UP ON THE ROOF

Words and Music by
GERRY GOFFIN and CAROLE KING

Flute/strings
16 beat
STYLE 002
Voice 300
Tempo 025-28

Slowly
N.C.

mp

G Em C D11 G Em C D11 G

When this old world starts a - get-ting me down and peo-ple are just too much for me to face, I'll climb way up to the top of the stairs and all my cares just drift right in - to space.

I come home feel-ing ti - red and beat, I'll go up where the air is fresh and sweet, I'll get far away from the hus-tl-ing crowd and all that rat race noise down in the street.

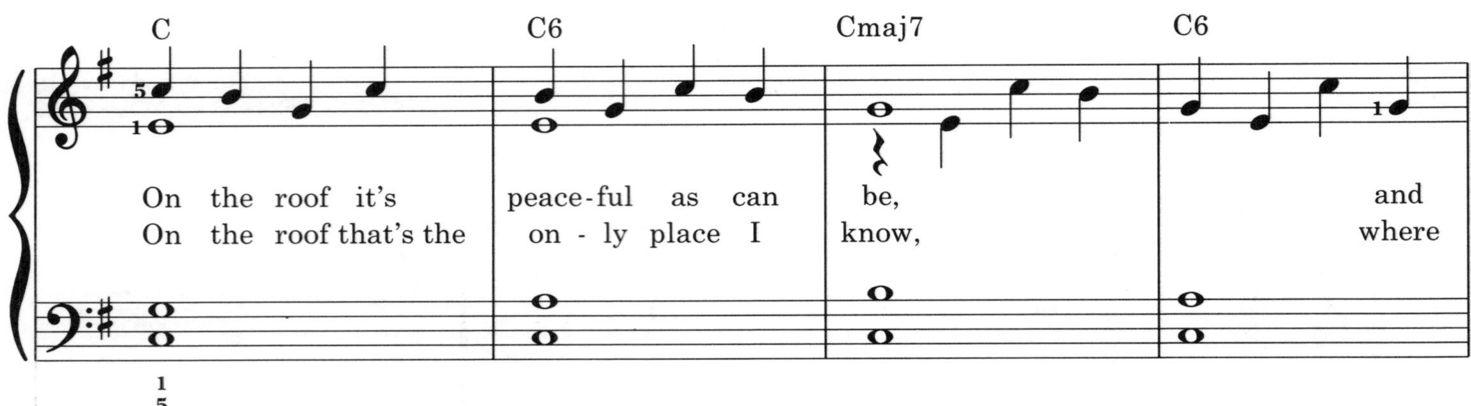
C
C6
Cmaj7
C6
On the roof it's peace-ful as can be, and
On the roof that's the on - ly place I know, where

G
Em7
C6
1.
D11 N.C.
there the world be - low don't bo - ther me.
So when
you just have to wish to make it so.

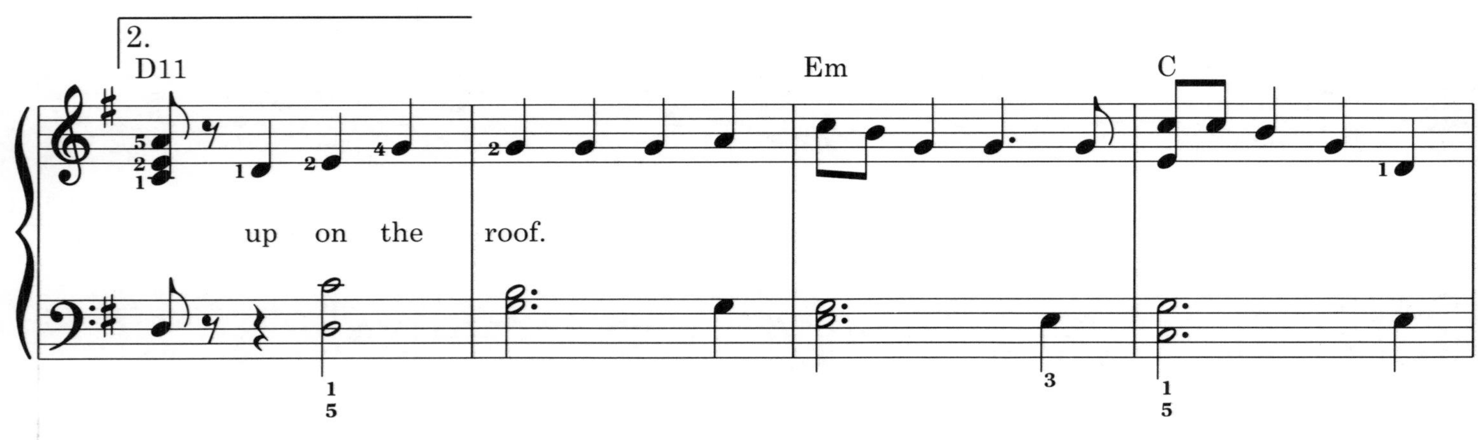
2.
D11
Em
C
up on the roof.

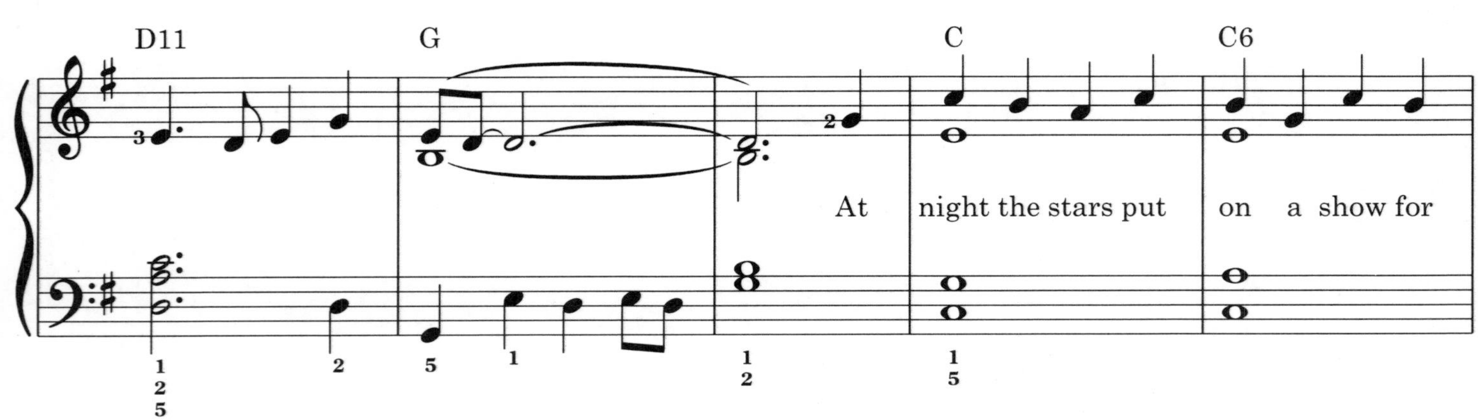
D11
G
C
C6
At night the stars put on a show for

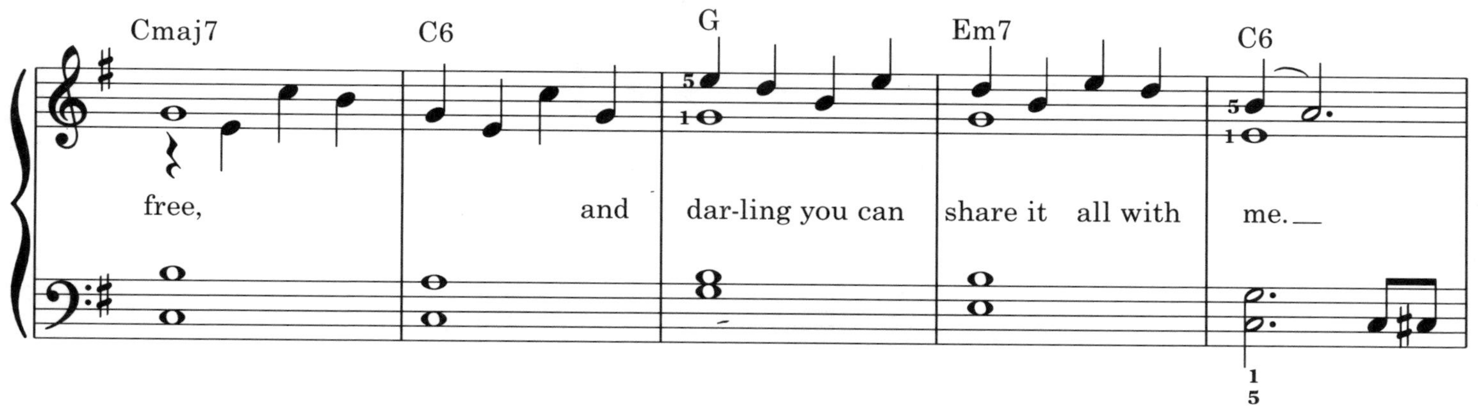

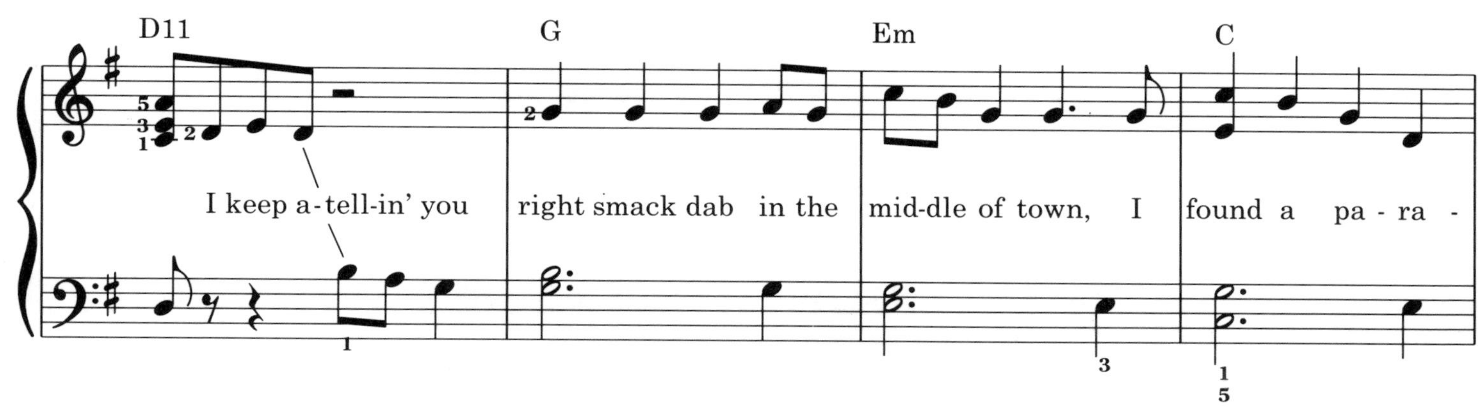

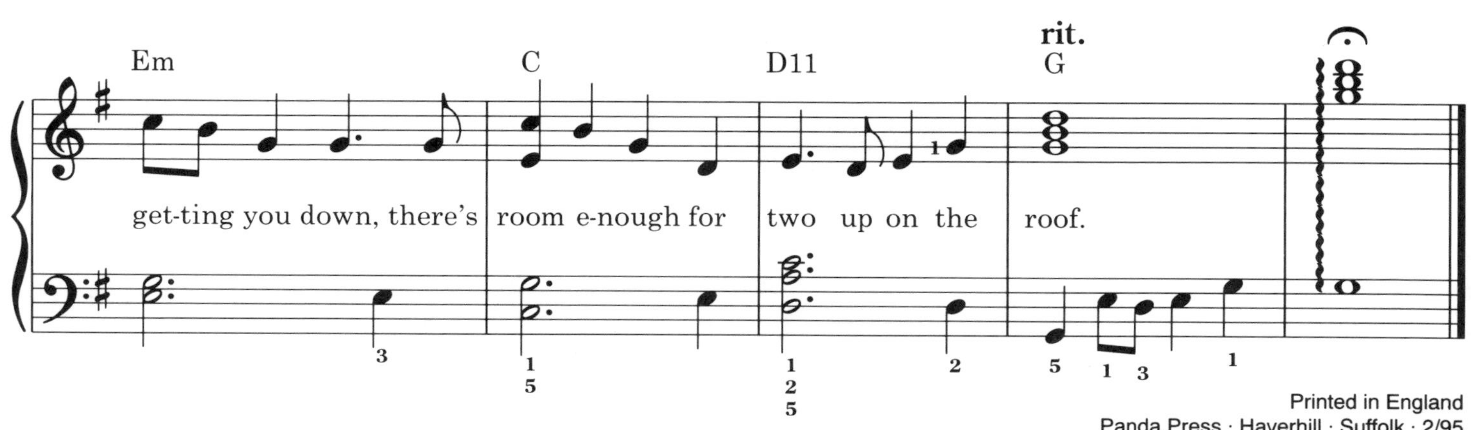

Printed in England
Panda Press · Haverhill · Suffolk · 2/95

Take it easy

LOVE SONGS

Always
Autumn Leaves (*Les Feuilles Mortes*)
Can't Stay Away From You
Close To You (They Long To Be)
Endless Love
The First Time Ever I Saw Your Face
Goodbye Girl
I'll Be There
I'm In The Mood For Love
The Power Of Love
Saving All My Love For You
Three Times A Lady
Will You Love Me Tomorrow?
You Are So Beautiful
You Needed Me

FILM CLASSICS

Eye Of The Tiger
Fame
Glory Of Love
I Have Nothing
It Must Have Been Love
(I've Had) The Time Of My Life
Philadelphia
Show Me Heaven
Take My Breath Away
Tears In Heaven
Theme From 'Superman'
Unchained Melody
Love Is In The Air

COUNTRY CLASSICS

Annie's Song
By The Time I Get To Phoenix
Constant Craving
Don't It Make My Brown Eyes Blue
Eagle When She Flies
Jolene
Lyin' Eyes
Outbound Plane
Standing Outside The Fire
Take It To The Limit
Take Me Home, Country Roads
Up On The Roof
Like A Sad Song

THE NINETIES

End Of The Road
Everybody's Talkin'
Get Here
Heal The World
Hero
I'll Stand By You
I Swear
A Million Love Songs
The Most Beautiful Girl In The World
Promise Me
Relight My Fire
Without You

CHILDREN'S TV FAVOURITES

The Banana Splits
Batman Theme
Blue Peter Theme (Barnacle Bill)
Hong Kong Phooey
The Magic Roundabout
(Meet) The Flintstones
Paddington Bear
Road Runner
Roobarb And Custard
Scooby Doo
Sesame Street
Thunderbirds
The Wombling Song
Yogi Bear
Postman Pat

SHOWTUNES

Another Openin', Another Show
Anything Goes
Cabaret
Edelweiss
Forty-Second Street
Getting To Know You
Hello Dolly
The Lady Is A Tramp
Let's Call The Whole Thing Off
This Can't Be Love
Thou Swell
True Love
Where Or When
With Every Breath I Take
If I Were a A Rich Man